Science for Children with Learning Difficulties

Macdonald Educational

A MACDONALD BOOK

The Learning Through Science Project

The authors of this material are:

Doug Kincaid
Helen Rapson
Roy Richards—Project Director

The other members of the Learning Through Science
team are:

John Allen
Margaret Collis

Artwork by Maggie Raynor
Front cover photograph by Fiona Pragoff

First published in Great Britain in 1983
Reprinted 1984, 1985, 1987, 1988

ISBN 0 356 09364 6

Printed and bound in Great Britain by
Purnell Book Production Ltd
A member of the BPCC Group

Published in Great Britain by
Macdonald & Co (Publishers) Ltd
Greater London House
Hampstead Road
London NW1 7QX
A BPCC plc company

CONTENTS

Acknowledgements

The Learning Through Science Project team are greatly indebted to the Local Education Authorities who have helped them work in their areas and to those teachers, heads, wardens, college of education staff and LEA representatives who have worked so hard on the team's behalf in furthering the work of children learning through science. For guidance we had our sponsors, our Monitoring Committee, the staff of Programme 3 at the Schools Council, and, for support in all our working, the University of London Goldsmiths' College. To all of them we acknowledge our many debts: their help has been invaluable.

Learning Through Science was a project jointly sponsored by the Schools Council and the Scottish Education Department, and based at the School of Education, University of London Goldsmiths' College. It is now under the aegis of the School Curriculum Development Committee. This project followed directly on from the Schools Council Science 5/13 Project. It aims at helping teachers to help children of primary and middle school age to learn science through first-hand experience.

One part of the work of the Learning Through Science Project has been the production of material to help teachers of children with learning difficulties. This followed the recommendation of the Warnock Committee that particular attention should be given to curriculum development for such children, and the revelation by Brennan that his team found science taught successfully to *slow learners* in only 4 of the 196 primary schools they visited in England and Wales.

Brennan concluded that one main requirement for improvement was the development of appropriate teaching materials and guidelines for teachers.

INTRODUCTION

Children with learning difficulties

The Warnock Committee recommended that the term *children with learning difficulties* should be used for all children who need some kind of special educational provision, apart from the gifted. (1)

The majority of these children are in ordinary schools, and the Committee concluded that 'a teacher of a mixed ability class of 30 children even in an ordinary school should be aware that possibly as many as six of them may require some form of special educational provision at some time during their school life and about four or five of them may require special educational provision at any given time'. Every teacher in primary and middle schools is likely to teach children with learning difficulties.

This material

This material has been written for the teachers of children who are at a concrete operational stage of thought, as defined by the Science 5/13 Project (3), and who are 'unable to manage learning tasks which are successfully completed by 75 to 80 per cent of their age peers'. (Brennan, 2) Most of these children are in ordinary schools. This material has been designed to be used very flexibly. It is hoped that teachers will select from it suitable work for their own pupils, and will modify and adapt it as necessary. No attempt has been made to cater for the particular problems of physically disabled children, or those with sensory handicaps, but it is hoped that their teachers will be able to use some of the ideas.

The material is presented in ten units. Each is based on topics drawn from those areas of science which many teachers consider to be important for primary and middle school children to learn about.

However, the units do *not* constitute a course or represent work which children *ought* to do. They are examples of the way scientific work can be planned and modified for children with learning difficulties, and it is hoped that teachers will develop other topics in a similar way. The units are complementary to the pupil material produced by the Learning Through Science team. (4) Many references are made to those pupil cards which could easily be modified by teachers for their children with learning difficulties.

Why science for children with learning difficulties?

Bullock (5) argues that science is 'an essential part of what should be every man's and every woman's educational birthright', and that 'the aspect of science as the greatest intellectual and cultural achievement of man is too often neglected'.

The scientific work that is done in primary and middle schools is particularly appropriate for children with learning difficulties. Essentially it involves first hand practical investigation of things concretely experienced, and is concerned with the objects and situations of everyday life.

In this work children use the distinctive method of scientific enquiry, making first hand observations – examining, comparing, measuring, sorting and classifying real things, finding similarities and differences, patterns and relationships; asking questions about their observations; devising tests to find the answers to the questions, predicting the results and then performing the tests – these are scientific experiments; recording the results of the tests, sorting and analysing them to see if their predictions were right and to find if their questions are answered; looking for patterns and relationships in the results of the tests; communicating to others what was done and found out.

This kind of practical investigation appeals to many children with learning difficulties, and often they do it very successfully. It has many benefits.*

It teaches children to think critically and objectively, to reason systematically, to assess evidence and to make their own judgments.

It gradually leads them to some understanding of scientific concepts such as cause and effect, energy, change, life cycle.

It fosters the development of important attitudes such as independence, perseverance, responsibility, self-criticism, open-mindedness.

It gives practice in manipulative skills, for instance in the construction and use of simple apparatus and models. It helps to develop social skills, as children working in a group or team learn to co-operate.

It gives strong motivation for the growth and purposeful use of literacy and mathematical skills.

Despite these many advantages, science is rarely included effectively in the curriculum of children with learning difficulties. (Brennan, 2) The material that has been produced by this project is an attempt to help teachers to remedy this situation.

What are the reasons for school failure?

The multiplicity of reasons for school failure highlights the problems of teaching children who have learning difficulties.

The reasons most often put forward as obstacles to school progress are listed below. Serious learning difficulties are often the result of a combination of several factors. The children may:

    have a low level of academic intelligence;
    come from a culturally dissonant background;
    come from unstable families and/or be given
    inadequate family care;
    be emotionally disturbed;
    have specific learning difficulties, such as poor
    co-ordination;
    have speech and/or language disorders;
    have physical or sensory handicaps;
    have been persistently absent from school;
    have a poor educational history resulting from:
        inefficient teaching;
        inappropriate teaching;
        low teacher expectation;
        unco-ordinated curricular content;
        poor parent-teacher relations.

Teachers will recognise many of the physical, mental and behavioural disabilities of their pupils. It is important that the factors contributing to a poor educational history are also examined.

*See also Learning Through Science: Formulating a School Policy (6)

What are the educational needs of children with learning difficulties?

All children have similar educational needs, and some of the following points have wide application. Others arise from the particular problems of children with learning difficulties.

1. All children thrive on success. Children with learning difficulties often grow to expect to fail, and often their teachers expect them to fail. In order to make progress *they must succeed, and be expected to succeed.*

2. It is especially important for children with learning difficulties to *understand that they make a real contribution to the work of their class.* Knowledge that they do this develops their self esteem, gives them personal satisfaction and pride, and helps to lead to responsible behaviour. Acceptance by their peers as valued contributors is important for their emotional development, as well as for their confidence in their capacity to learn.

3. *They need to be shown what is interesting in their world,* so that their curiosity and desire to learn are stimulated. Because they may be disruptive or slow, they may be excluded from the very things that would interest them, such as visits and practical classroom activities. They need vivid links with their environment.

4. *Their cognitive development must be encouraged* by many varied opportunities to work with concrete materials and to use all their senses. They need to notice, compare and test, and to have their attention drawn to similarities and relationships. However, concrete work must not be regarded as an end in itself, but as giving the child a basis for reasoning and making generalisations, so that concepts are steadily expanded.

5. They need practical work to help them to *develop physical control,* and interactions with other people *to promote their social skills.*

6. *Their learning is often best organised into small steps,* quickly attained, with *frequent repetition and reinforcement* in many guises. Periodical interesting revision helps the children to assimilate knowledge.

7. Most children with learning difficulties lack literacy skills. They may be retarded in spoken language, they are usually far behind their chronological age in reading, and many have difficulty in writing. It is important that their lack of these skills does not preclude the children from interesting and exciting practical activities. However, if they are not to become disappointed and frustrated it may be *desirable to avoid giving them written instructions, and to devise ways in which they can easily record the measurements and results of their work.*

8. *Realistic objectives should be set* for each child. For this to be done, *records are necessary.*
(i) A day to day record of the work the child has done.
(ii) Periodical measurement and assessment of the child's progress in learning, and evaluation of the results in relation to the objectives which had been set for him previously.

9. Children with learning difficulties need *frequent contact with their teacher,* and constant encouragement and reassurance.

How does the material of this project attempt to meet these needs in relation to science?

Refer to the numbered paragraphs in the left-hand column

A. *The units are written for teachers,* it is not intended that children should use them directly. — 7, 9

B. *Each unit attempts to bring out the processes of science* – observing, ordering, questioning, devising and using fair tests, recording results and using them to answer the questions, looking for patterns and relationships. — 4, 5

C. *The topics arise from the children's interests or everyday surroundings,* and integrate well with the rest of the curriculum. — 3

D. Most of the units present *a variety of short practical investigations – the teacher is asked to choose* suitable work for his own pupils. — 1, 2, 6, 9

E. Practical methods are suggested, but *children are encouraged to develop and extend the work in ways which interest them.* — 4, 5

F. *It presents ideas and experiences in a number of different ways* to help to reinforce the children's understanding. — 6

G. *It suggests simple and quick recording methods.* — 7

H. *It puts forward some discussion points* to help teachers to bring out scientific ideas and to look for patterns and relationships. — 4, 9

There is a chapter on record keeping in *Learning Through Science: Formulating a School Policy.* (5) — 8

A review of the organisation for children with learning difficulties in ordinary schools, with reference to science

Current practice in primary and middle schools seems to include three main methods of organisation for children with learning difficulties:
the children may work for part of the time in *special classes*;
they may normally work in mixed ability classes from which they are periodically *withdrawn for special (remedial) teaching*;
they may work in *mixed ability classes*.

Organisation in mixed ability classes may be:
in mixed ability groups;
in streamed groups;
in streamed sets across a year.

Special classes
With falling roles and fewer teachers these seem to be less common than they were. Brennan (2) considered that at least two special classes were needed by a junior or middle school if the children were to benefit, a single class was rarely successful... and usually took on the distressing features of a sink class'.
Special classes are usually very small; the teacher has time to work with individuals; the best approach and material can be used without danger of the children feeling that they are being given simpler work than their peers or talked down to. However, without the standard set by a mixed class, the children are often not stretched, and the stimulation that comes from interaction with more able children is missing.

Mixed ability classes with remedial withdrawal teaching
Children are very commonly withdrawn for remedial work in literacy skills, reading in particular. Some schools give extra help with mathematics.
It has been suggested that remedial teachers should make much more use of scientific work with their groups, not only because of the benefits described on page 5, but also because of the great stimulus it gives to learning those basic skills with which these teachers are most concerned – talking, reading, writing and mathematical skills.
If possible, children should not be taken out for remedial work when interesting and stimulating practical things are happening in their ordinary classes, for these activities are also vital for their progress.
Occasionally the remedial teacher works in the ordinary classroom, instead of withdrawing the children. This seems to be unusual, but could be a valuable means of helping children with learning difficulties in many parts of the curriculum.

Mixed ability classes with no extra help for children with learning difficulties
In mixed ability groups
A variety of constraints influences the way a teacher forms his groups, but if a class has 5 or 6 children with learning difficulties it is likely that one will be in each group.
Brennan (2) commented 'Whatever the merits of mixed ability teaching for pupils making normal progress... it was the considered opinion of the project team that they had not observed the curricular needs of slow learners being satisfactorily met within this kind of school organisation'.
It has been remarked that in this situation a child with learning difficulties is usually given either simpler work than the rest of his group, or the same work but less is expected of him. Provided the rest of his group is willing to help him, it is assumed that the slow child is making adequate progress. However, he may actually learn very little. He often thinks he understands when he does not, and may easily be overlooked by a busy teacher.

In streamed groups
Some teachers feel that this gives the best opportunity to children of all levels of ability. It is also a way in which children often tend to organise themselves.
It is suggested that advantages for the child with learning difficulties are that the teacher sees at once if the child does not understand the work to be done; the child does not feel that any of the activities of his group are beyond him, and he cannot *hide* behind more able children; and the teacher discusses the group's work in the way best suited to such children.
Against this is the danger of children feeling that they are being given simpler work than their peers, thus reinforcing their own belief in their backwardness, which would tend to exacerbate behaviour problems. Also, as has been pointed out earlier, the children's poor peformance will be due to a wide variety of reasons, and the work needed by an intelligent child who is under-achieving may be very different from that needed by a dull child.
A vital factor for success is the recognition by the group of children with learning difficulties (and by the rest of the class) of the value of the work it is doing.

Streamed sets across a year
In some junior and middle schools the children in a year group are put into streamed sets for certain subjects, particularly mathematics and English.
By this method of organisation, children with different levels of performance are separated even more sharply than when streamed groups are formed within a class.
It is unusual for year groups to be put into sets for science, although it does happen in the third and fourth years of some middle schools, where it is considered to be a useful introduction to secondary school practice. Sets normally operate within a very rigid time-table, which is more suited to a secondary school approach to science than to a primary approach.

Bibliography

1. Warnock Committee	Special Educational Needs: Report of the Committee of Enquiry into the Education of Handicapped Children and Young People *(The Warnock Report)*, HMSO, 1978.
2. Brennan, W.K.	*Curricular needs of slow learners*, Schools Council Working Paper 63, Evans Methuen, 1979.
3. Schools Council	*With objectives in mind*, Guide to Science 5-13, Macdonald Educational, 1972.
4. Schools Council	Learning Through Science pupil materials: *Ourselves*, 1981, *Colour*, 1981, *Materials*, 1982, *Sky and Space*, 1982, *All Around*, 1982, *Out of Doors*, 1982, *On the Move*, 1983, *Moving Around*, 1983, *Electricity*, 1983, *Earth*, 1983, *Time, Growth and Change*, 1984, *Which and What?*, 1984, Macdonald Educational.
5. Bullock, Lord	*School Science Review*, vol. 57, No. 201, June 1976. Presidential address to the Association for Science Education.
6. Schools Council	*Learning Through Science, Formulating a School Policy*, Macdonald Educational, 1980.

Other important references

Gulliford, R.	*Backwardness and Educational Failure*, NFER, 1969.
Tansley A.E. and Gulliford, R.	*Education of Slow Learning Children*, RKP, 1960.

ME AND MY FRIENDS

Contents

This section shows how a child with learning difficulties can build up a book about himself or herself. A stitched book about 40 centimetres square is envisaged. It also shows how the findings from the various activities carried out by each individual can be related to other children.

My portrait, and face shapes

For children to do individually

The first page of each child's book can start with *a portrait*. It can be drawn or painted, or a photograph could be used. It can be a self-portrait or a portrait painted by another child. Children often paint reasonably recognisable self-portraits with the help of a mirror. Talk about the face with the children and feel different parts of the face as well as looking at these parts. Look too, for their relationship to each other, for example, eyes are usually parallel with ears.

For children to do as a group

We all have differently-shaped faces. Making a pictorial chart to illustrate this, helps us concentrate on head features.

Face shapes can be cut from sugar paper, noses and mouths cut from coloured sticky paper, and hair made from strands of wool. It is also possible to identify shape by drawing round faces on a mirror with a Chinagraph pencil.

Six shapes may be too difficult for some children to handle. You may want to concentrate on round, square and rectangular faces only.

To discuss

How face shapes vary. (Variation is an important biological concept.) Talk about the different face shapes, talk about detail. How do eye shapes vary; are some noses broad, some long, some Roman?
Who has bushy eyebrows, who has cupid bow lips? How are we all different, yet all alike?

See Learning Through Science, *Ourselves*, the card *Heads and Faces*, Macdonald, 1981.

My profile silhouette

For children to do individually

Let each child make a profile silhouette of a friend. Position a child and an Anglepoise lamp or projector so that a shadow of the child's profile is cast as accurately as possible on a wall.

The drawing sheet must be firmly pinned to the wall, and a darkened room is best. The child doing the drawing may need help. Cut out and fill in the shape carefully with black paint. You can use paper which is white one side and black the other. Reversing the white cut-out gives you a black silhouette.

For children to do as a group

Do some extra silhouettes and mount them as a group frieze.

Can children guess who is who?

To discuss

How the shape of the silhouette varies depending both on the position of the sitter and the position of the light source. How the silhouette picture helps emphasise certain facial features. (It also shows up hair shapes and styles well, and these are distinctive features of any person.) How the head shapes of brothers and sisters are often similar.

Facts and figures

For children to do individually

Children are fascinated with facts about themselves, everything from how heavy they are to the colour of their hair. For children with learning difficulties the questionnaire should be brief, but some children may like to extend it. Addresses, favourite foods, names of pets and so on can be recorded, but be careful about prying into personal matters.

The family tree will help children with ordering. Who is the oldest member of the family? Who is the youngest? Who is the oldest brother or sister? Relationships are difficult for many children to understand. They will need much discussion, and often this will need to be of a sensitive nature. There are, for example, one parent families.

For children to do as a group
All the usual work on charting and graphing can be done. For example.

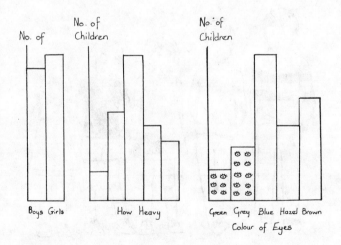

To discuss
The important thing, of course, is to use the charts to find patterns and relationships. Which is the commonest eye colour? Which is the commonest height? Who is the heaviest child?

See Learning Through Science, *Ourselves*, the card *Facts about Me*, Macdonald, 1981.

Little and large

For children to do individually

As well as their height children can measure the height to which they can reach, and the height to which they can jump.

Children can also try to make themselves as small as possible. Make a *dart board* target with overlapping sheets of paper. Use a string, drawing pin and pencil to draw the circles.

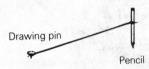

Drawing pin

Pencil

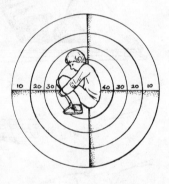

Name	Score
Jane	30
John	20
Sarah	40

Vary the diameter of the circle to suit the range of heights of children in your class.

Those who tuck themselves into the smallest space score most.

Who can make themselves small enough to go *under* the jumping bar? Can anyone do it limbo-dancing-style?

To discuss
Does the tallest person reach the furthest? Does the tallest person leap the highest? Does the largest person tuck himself into the largest ball? Does the smallest child make the smallest ball?

See Learning Through Science, *Ourselves*, the card *Leg Power*, Macdonald, 1981.

Hands and feet

For children to do
Ask the children to make some hand prints. Use a thin flat, kitchen sponge soaked in powder paint. Put newspaper underneath. The *give* in the newspaper helps to make a good print. Spread the fingers as wide as possible. To obtain the area of the hand draw round it on to squared paper and count the squares.

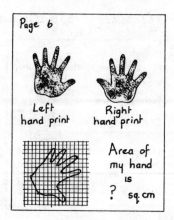

Page 6

Left hand print

Right hand print

Area of my hand is ? sq. cm

Sponge

Newspaper

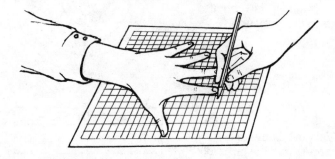

Use the same technique to print with feet. Footprints that have been cut out can be used to measure the length and width of the classroom. Compare the measurements with those obtained by using a tape-measure.

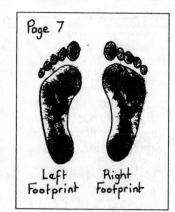

Page 7

Left Footprint

Right Footprint

To discuss
The pattern of the hand and footprints. The police now take palm prints as well as fingerprints.
Compare flat feet with those with a good instep. (Don't hurt anyone's feelings.)

See Learning Through Science, *Ourselves*, the cards *Handy Things*, and *Feet and Footwear*, Macdonald, 1981.

Fingers and friends

Fingers vary in length, thickness and skin pattern. Investigate length.

For children to do individually
Draw carefully around the middle and little fingers. Cut each out and decorate it as a finger *friend*. Use felt tips, and paper or fabric collage to decorate each *friend*. Do some extra ones for class use.

Page 8

My finger friends

For children to do as a class or group
Arrange the middle fingers in order size. Do the same for the small fingers.

Do the tallest children have the longest middle fingers? Stand children in a row based on height. Is there a match with finger size?

To discuss
The variation in size of fingers; look for a pattern between finger length and height. Is the middle finger always the longest?

See Learning Through Science, *Ourselves*, the card *Fingers*, Macdonald, 1981.

Hands tell

For children to do individually

Hands can be used to tell us many things. They can point the way. Tell us to stop.

Page 9

Litter Here

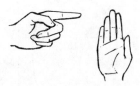

Children can draw round a hand onto paper and use the cut-out to show these things.

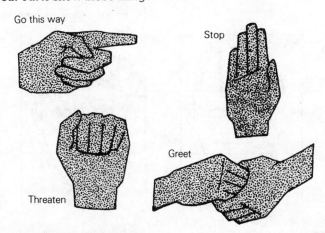

Go this way

Stop

Threaten

Greet

For children to do as a group

All these hand signs are means of communication.

A pointed hand could be pinned up in school to indicate the way to the hall.

HALL

Invent other signs to put around the school. What would you use for the Head's room, staffroom, toilets, boiler room, classroom?

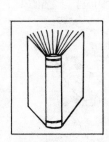

To discuss

Ways of communication. Road signs. What triangular and circular signs mean.

Print it

For children to do individually

Make some fingerprints. Try one of these methods. Try different inks: writing, drawing, printing, Indian. Try different paints: poster, acrylic, powder. Try different kinds of paper: tissue, writing, newspaper, sugar paper.

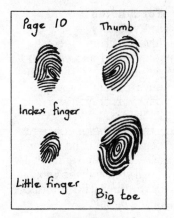

Page 10

Thumb

Index finger

Little finger

Big toe

Methods to try.

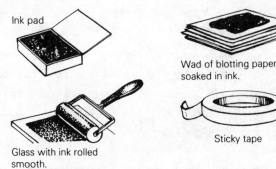

Ink pad

Wad of blotting paper soaked in ink.

Glass with ink rolled smooth.

Sticky tape

Sort the fingerprints into groups.

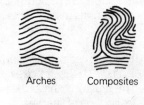

Loops   Whorls   Arches   Composites

Enlarge one of the prints by freely painting it as a brush pattern. Try printing flowers with finger and thumbprints.
Or print a swarm of flies. They could be on a flypaper.

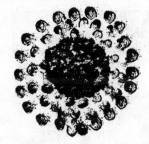

To discuss

Is one pattern of fingerprint more common? Do the fingers on one hand have the same pattern? Do fingers on the right-hand have the same pattern as those on the left?

It's all done by touch

For children to do individually

Investigate and record texture and surface differences in the environment. Use a dark wax crayon and kitchen paper to discover as many *tactile* surfaces as possible. Hold the paper flat on each surface and rub a small area with the wax crayon until it is reproduced on the paper.

Natural	Artificial
Rough	Smooth

Collect and mount as many samples as possible. You might classify them in contrasting groups such as natural or man-made, rough or smooth. Encourage the children to mount collections in their books.

How difficult is it to distinguish things by touch? Use *blind* bags or boxes (bags or boxes you can put your hand in but not see in). Put in: coins; odds and ends; a collection of small toys; a collection of shapes.

You could make the tests more difficult, for example, sort grades of sandpaper.

Coarse   Medium   Fine   Extra fine

To discuss

The sensitivity of the fingertips in differentiating between different surfaces. Are nail-biters less sensitive?

See Learning Through Science, *Ourselves*, the cards *With Feeling*, and *It's a Nerve*, Macdonald, 1981.

Wanted

For children to do

An identikit picture can be made by drawing or painting. Provide an oval shaped template for children to use. Let each child draw round the template. Divide the outline drawing into three roughly equal parts.

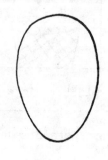
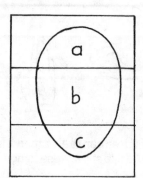

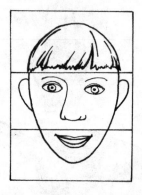

Draw the top of the head in section a, the eyes and nose in section b, and the mouth and chin in section c.

Ask each child to write his or her name in each of the three sections on the back of each sheet. Cut each drawing or painting into three pieces. Mix up the identikit pieces from several children. Can the children sort out the right eyes to go with the right mouth and so on? This makes a useful sorting and separating exercise.

Ask each child to make a poster of his best friend.

To discuss

How face details vary.

Chomp away

E for easy

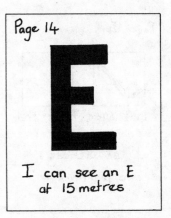

> Page 13
> Teeth are used for
>   biting
>   chewing
>   talking
>   whistling
>   smiling

> Page 14
>
> **E**
>
> I can see an E at 15 metres

For children to do individually

Teeth are used for many things.

Make a moving mouth puppet. It will help focus attention on the up and down movement of the jaw. Use a piece of card 20 x 15 cm. Part folded it usually retains some quality of spring.

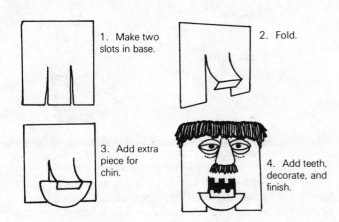

1. Make two slots in base.
2. Fold.
3. Add extra piece for chin.
4. Add teeth, decorate, and finish.

Use the puppets to devise dialogue for a play.

For children to do as a group

All this jaw action is to chop up food. Teeth are vital in this function, but how many children look after their teeth? Make a survey. How many children clean their teeth?

Never	Not very often	Sometimes	Nearly every day	Every day

To discuss

The importance of teeth in smiling, biting, chewing, talking, singing, whistling. Care of teeth. Different kinds of teeth.

See Learning Through Science, *Ourselves*, the card *Open Wide*, Macdonald, 1981.

For children to do as a group

Make a large chart approximately 60 x 80 cm. Mark this with letter E's. Vary the orientation of the letter. Make a large cut out letter E that a child can hold.

One child points to a letter E on the chart. The child being tested holds up the letter E to match the one indicated.

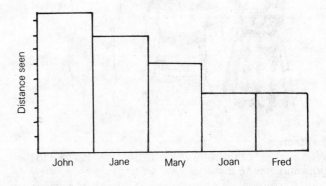

Start the testing at about 2 metres. Keep on testing at greater and greater distances. When a child can no longer match the E's you have a measure of their seeing ability over a distance. Record this distance. It could be done with a piece of string run from the chart to the child.

Chart the results in order of seeing ability.

John	Jane	Mary	Joan	Fred

Distance seen

To discuss

How we all vary in our seeing ability, hence the need for spectacles. The test can be taken further. Are right eyes better than left eyes? How does the light affect the test?

See Learning Through Science, *Ourselves*, the card *Eye Tests*, Macdonald, 1981.

Seeing sideways

Page 15

Left 60cm   Right 40cm

I saw these
two pictures

For children to do as a group

It is surprising what we can all see out of the corners of our eyes. Children can investigate whether some of them have wider-angled vision than others. Put up a line of pictures at the front of the class. A child sits in a chair about half a metre away from the pictures. This child must look fixedly ahead and say which pictures are visible. To prevent inadvertent head turning two other children should stand either side and hold the victim's head steady.

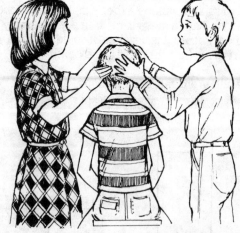

To discuss

Who has best peripheral vision in the class? How far to the right and how far to the left can *most* children see? Why good peripheral vision is useful, for example to a driver or to a pedestrian watching for traffic. The width of vision in other animals. A fish and a bird, for example, can see almost all around them for they have eyes at the sides of their heads.

See Learning Through Science, *Ourselves*, the card *Why Two Eyes?*, Macdonald, 1981.

It's coloured

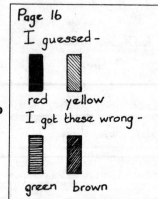

Page 16
I guessed –

red   yellow
I got these wrong –

green   brown

For children to do as a group

Make a range of colour test cards from coloured sugar paper. Use red, green, yellow, blue, orange, brown, black and white. Cut out pieces 5 cm square and then cut them in half.

Choose a place where you can test them over a long distance either outside or in a long corridor or in the school. The child carrying out the test holds up each piece of coloured sugar paper in turn. The child being tested holds up what he or she thinks is the corresponding half. It may prove best to hold a piece of grey card behind each colour to act as a neutral background. Keep a record of which colours were correctly identified.

| Name | Coloured paper | | | |
	Red	Yellow	Green	Blue
John	✔	✔	✔	✗

To discuss

Which colours show up best over a distance. If it is possible, try it on a bright day and a dull day. Talk about which colours *travel* well. In urban areas you can take a walk around the town and see which colours advertisers prefer to use in hoardings.

See Learning Through Science, *Colour*, the cards *Looking at Colour, Colourful Us, Colour in the Street*, Macdonald, 1981 and *Get the Message*, page 73.

Listen hard

For children to do individually
Make a collection of objects that will make a noise.

For children to do as a group
Sit the group around a large mat in the hall. Spread the objects out on the mat.

Ask each child, in turn, to pick an object and make a sound with it. Talk about the sound produced each time. Now ask the children to sit with their backs to the objects. Make a sound with each one in turn. Can they guess which object makes the sound?

You can make the game more difficult by making noises with objects that the children have not been allowed to see beforehand.

To discuss
Why the children think some of the objects are more difficult to identify by sound alone than others. Is it familiarity with the object and its sound that helps? Are loud sounds easier to tell than quieter ones? Are high sounds more distinctive than low ones?

See Learning Through Science, *Ourselves*, the card *Listen!*, Macdonald, 1981.

Smelling and tasting

For children to do

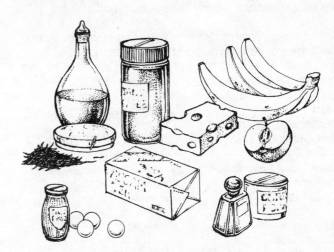

Collect a range of substances with a distinctive smell. For example, tea, chopped grass, perfume, coffee, fish paste, moth-balls, shoe polish, banana, apple, cheese, vinegar, curry powder. Select four things. Can children guess these by smell alone? Choose another four things. Test again. Which are we best at guessing? Is it the ones with which we are most familiar?

Collect a range of things to taste. For example, carrot, turnip, swede, cheese, apple, banana, grape, onion, chocolate, salt, crisps, tomato sauce, tea, coffee. Let children try a number of these on their friends. They may find it makes the test fairer if all the foods are chopped so that texture does not give clues to naming the foods. Try the test again but this time with children holding their noses as they taste each food.

To discuss
How *familiarity* with the things we smell helps us to recognise them. The link between smell and taste. Terms to describe taste, e.g. sweet, sour, cool, sharp, hot, cold, creamy, tasteless, soft, hard, raw, cooked.

See Learning Through Science, *Ourselves*, the cards *Smell and Scents* and *Tasty Things*, Macdonald, 1981.

More to do

There are *many* other aspects of *Me and my friends* worth pursuing with children who have learning difficulties.

The Learning Through Science pack *Ourselves* contains the following cards (*in addition* to those mentioned in this text), for slow learning children. They will help to add many more pages to any child's *Book about Me*.

Card	Further work on
Remember, Remember	Memory
How Quick are You?	Reaction Times
Inside Story	The Body
Dem Bones, Dem Bones	
Puffing and Blowing	Breathing
Hear, Hear	Listening
Pin-pointing Sounds	
Why two eyes?	Looking
About Eyes	
Handy Things	Arms and Legs
How Do You rate?	Facts about Me
Hot and Cold	

ME AND MY SHADOW
ME AND MY REFLECTION

This section is intended to help children with learning difficulties to explore space, time, movement and pattern. It does so through the use of shadows and reflections.

Contents

Play with shadows

Many children confuse shadows with reflections. The following *games* will help bring about some understanding of the nature of a shadow. Shadows change, they are sometimes long and thin, sometimes short and fat, sometimes clear, and sometimes faint. In playing with shadows children will become more aware of these changes. Such play also takes children into an exploration of space and time and movement.

For children to do

Make a long shadow. Who can make the longest one?	Make a short shadow. Who can make the shortest one?

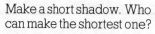

Make a funny shaped shadow.	Shake hands. What does your shadow do?

Whose is the funniest?	Can you get your shadows to shake hands without your own hands touching.
Hide your shadow.	Can you move without your shadow moving? Stand with your shadow in front of you. Stand with your shadow behind you. Touch your shadow.

Jump on your shadow.	Make a shadow with four arms, six arms, six legs.

To discuss
Talk about what a shadow looks like. Talk about how the shadow length can vary in relation to the height of the object. Try and bring out how in all the above experiences the relationship between sun and object and shadow are fixed.

Shadows from things

Try using objects to make shadows.

For children to do
Move the objects each time to make the largest and the smallest shadow you can.

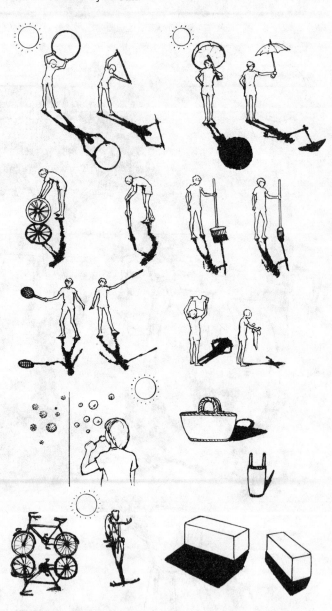

Make the drawings of some of the shadows cast. Either draw round them with chalk, or draw them in pencil on paper.

To discuss
Children will have *discovered* that the angle at which light falls on a particular object will affect the shape of its shadow. This will be a difficult concept for many of them to master but the experiences will give them a sound *feel* for what is happening. It will be of considerable benefit to them to attempt to talk about what is happening. It is also helpful to take up how the sharpness of shadow varies with different weather conditions.

The sun as a light source

Throughout the experiences with shadows children will have become more and more aware that the sun is a source of light. Now will be the time to take more overt notice of this but warn the children *never* to look directly at the sun.

For children to do
Mark a window with sticky tape and chart the shadow cast down the wall by making crosses on mounted sheets of paper.

Alternatively trace the lines of shadow cast by a window frame.

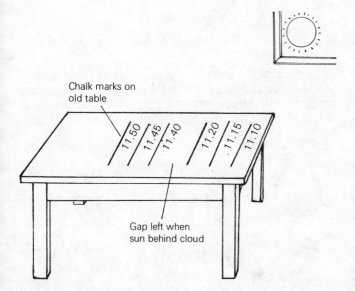

Chalk marks on old table

11.50 11.45 11.40 11.20 11.15 11.10

Gap left when sun behind cloud

To discuss
How the marks show the movement from east to west. How the sun is higher in the sky at some times of the year than at other times. You may want to carry out work on the cardinal points of the compass.

Recording shadows

Many children with learning difficulties have trouble making records. Charting shadows is relatively easy for them because they have only to draw around a changing shape as in the activities below.

For children to do

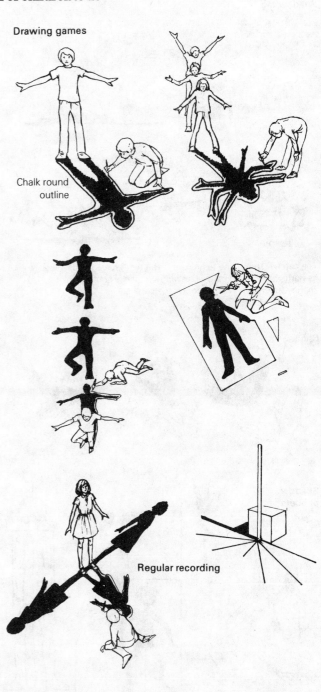

Drawing games

Chalk round outline

Regular recording

To discuss
The movement from west to east of the shadow can be discussed. It helps to ask the children to try and predict where a shadow will be at various times of the day. Repeating the exercise on another day with checks on predicted places for the shadow may prove an interesting game.

21

Shadows just for fun

These are other interesting games to play with shadows that would give much pleasure and at the same time provide a good learning experience.

For children to do

Shadow tag

Catch

Catcher

Team B

Team A

The catcher shouts the team name. The team runs, hands joined, to its home base. If the catcher's shadow touches another child's shadow, then that child becomes the catcher.

Shadow play

Shadow puppets

Still

Moving

40 cm high

To discuss

If you make shadow puppets then the light source (unlike the sun) can be varied. The effects of doing this on the shadows will be worth discussing. It is also useful to try out a double light source and thus get more than one shadow of an object.

Shadow box

For children to do

Make a *shadow box* to investigate shadows.

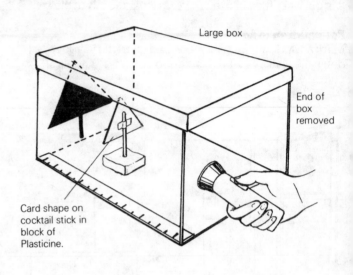

Large box

End of box removed

Card shape on cocktail stick in block of Plasticine.

What kind of shadow do these card shapes make?

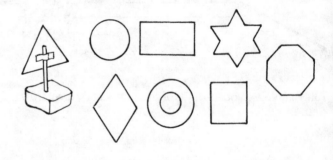

Can you cast a shadow exactly the same size as the shape? Can you make it twice as big as the shape? Can you make it smaller than the shape? What happens when you rotate the shape. Mould some solid shapes from Plasticine. Try them out.

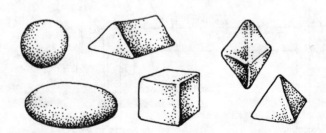

To discuss

The relationship between the size of the shadow cast and the distance of the shape from *screen* and torch. The relationship between the form of shadow cast and the angle at which the shape is placed to the light.

Reflections

For children to do
Many children confuse shadows with reflections. Begin with making a collection of things that give reflections. Encourage the children to help.

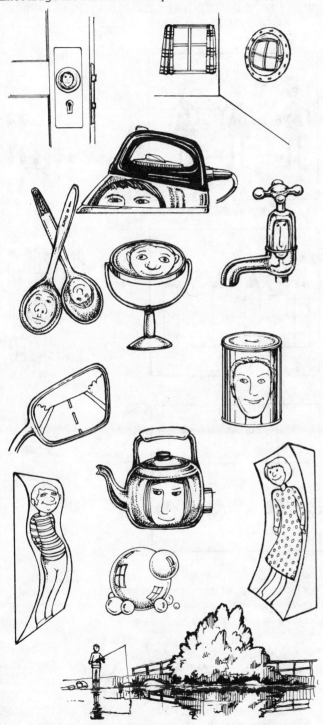

Draw the faces seen in some of the objects. Choose a variety of distortions to draw.

To discuss
Discuss how *shiny* surfaces reflect light well. Talk about curved surfaces giving distorted images and sometimes reversed images.

Playing with mirrors

A lot can be learned about the reflection of light by playing with mirrors.

For children to do
Use a mirror.

Look at the sky. Be careful. Do not look at the sun.

Look behind you.

Look round corners.

Look over things.

Play light spot tag.

Chase *spots* with *spots*. Make the *spot* follow a line such as the mortar in a wall. Draw geometric shapes on the wall. Trace the outlines of these with your *spots*.

To discuss
Talk about what you can see in the mirror and how you must move it to see different things.

It's all done with mirrors

For children to do
Ask children to look at themselves in a mirror.

Touch an ear.

Touch a nose.

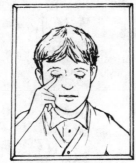

Touch an eyelid.

Ask them to print their name, looking in a mirror to do so.

Can they invent a shield to prevent cheating, that is a sheet of card held above the writing hand.

Take a sheet of paper, fold it through the centre and print a name along the fold. Do this with thick paint. Take the offset print. Make a class montage of name pattern reflections made in this way.

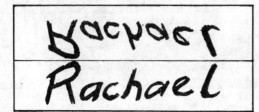

To discuss
The mirror reversal that emerges from these exercises is the obvious point to discuss. How much can the children see a pattern in their observations? Look for letters which are reversed and for those which come out as normal.

More with mirrors

For children to do
Ask the children to use their mirrors on patterns like these. Draw them on the blackboard for the children to copy. They will need to draw them to a size suitable for whatever mirrors they are using. They can invent their own patterns once they are used to the idea.

Use the mirror

to make

to make

to make

to make

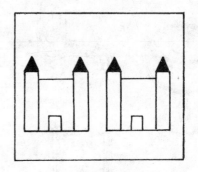

to make

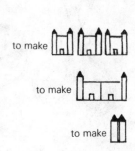

to make

to make

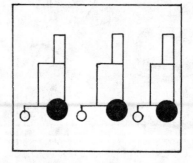

to make

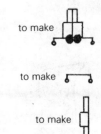

to make

to make

Ask children to put the mirror on the circle centre. Twist it about. Look at the patterns made. Draw one of them. Colour it.

To discuss
How patterns can be made to repeat themselves. What a mirror can change, for example shape. What a mirror cannot change, for example colour.

On reflection

The experience gained of mirror images will be very useful but can be difficult for children with learning difficulties to understand. The tests will need to be repeated many times. The following exercises may also help them gain further understanding.

For children to do
Most children play a game *Simon says* or *O'Grady says*. When a person performs an action another has to repeat the action provided it is prefaced by 'Simon says'. Note that when one person raises a right arm the other raises his or hers. There is no copying in a *reflective* sense.

Get the children to play this game. *Leave* them to *play*. I. and P. Opie in *Children's Games in Street and Playground*, O.U.P., 1969, quote J. Locke when he says 'it was Liberty alone which gives the true Relish and Delight to their ordinary Play Games.'

Now interfere. Give them a new rule. They must *mirror copy* the presenters actions or they are out.

To discuss
How one game differs from the other. The second game is like making a reflection in a mirror.

Back to mirrors

For children to do
Try these things.

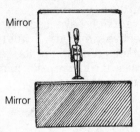

Look over the top of one mirror into the other. How many images of the toy soldier can you see? Can you count the images? Are they all the same size?

Make multiple images with mirrors at an angle. Vary the angle. What do children find happens?

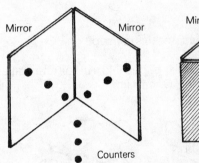 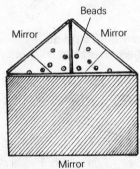

Put three mirrors together (a kaleidoscope). Put in coloured beads.

Make a periscope. Take a cube of wood. Cut diagonally. Glue handbag mirrors to the diagonal faces. Nail on two strips of wood for the side pieces.

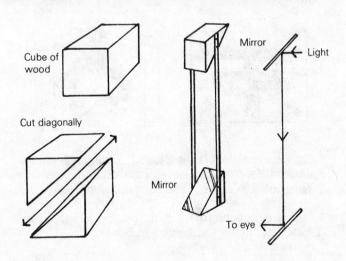

To discuss
The idea of repeated images. Where the angle between two mirrors is varied children will find the number of images varies too. Can they work out a relationship between the number of images and the angle between the mirrors? Talk about the pathway the light takes in a periscope.

Discuss the use of two mirrors on a dressing table, a curved mirror placed for seeing round a road corner, the dentist's mirror.

Reflective symmetry

From the experiences gained with using mirrors children will probably have discovered that objects can show reflective symmetry. If a mirror is placed along the axis of symmetry of an object the shape will appear unchanged because the image of the mirror will correspond with the half that is obscured.

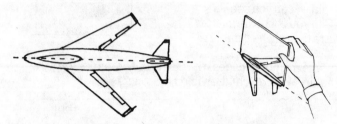

For children to do
These exercises will reinforce this concept.

1. Take a sheet of rectangular paper, fold it in half and make tears around the free edge. Open it up.

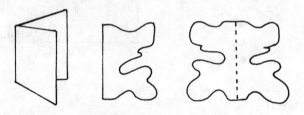

2. Using coloured inks make blots on a paper folded vertically through the centre. Convert these to symmetrical patterns by folding and pressing. Make a blot monster book with blot patterns.

3. Collect examples of natural forms showing reflective symmetry. For example, leaves, petals, mini-beasts. Where possible, make rubbings or prints with them.

4. Look at a collection of common objects. Draw them and decide whether they are symmetrical or not.

To discuss
How symmetrical shapes show a pattern of reflection along a central axis.

Rotational symmetry

All shapes when turned will repeat themselves after a full turn (360°). Many of the mirror activities will have brought out that some forms will do this in intermediate positions. For example on every quarter or half turn. These shapes show rotational symmetry about a centre of rotation.

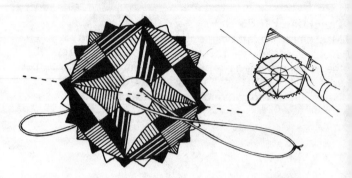

For children to do
1. Test shapes with a mirror to see if they possess rotational symmetry.

Draw a wheel.   Draw round a saucer.

Draw round a tin lid.   Draw a clock face.

2. Collect and print with shapes which have rotational symmetry: spools, cylinders, containers.

3. Look for natural forms that show rotational symmetry and make and display a collection. Flowers are an obvious choice.

To discuss
How objects show a pattern around a centre of rotation.

Translational symmetry

Reflectional symmetry can be taken further by *repeating* a pattern along a line. In nature this repeated pattern is seen well in the segments of a caterpillar. It is called translational symmetry.

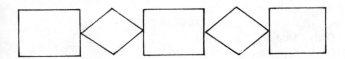

For children to do
Look for suitable shapes or use a cut potato to print examples of translational symmetry, for example a weird caterpillar.

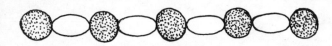

1. Make a frieze of potato cut caterpillars on symmetrical cabbages.

2. Make a printed picture of the life cycle of a butterfly.

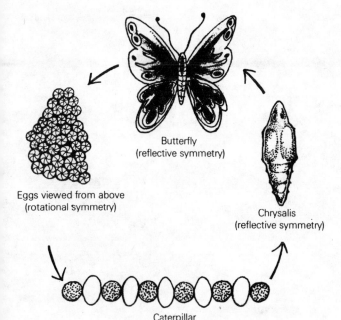

Butterfly
(reflective symmetry)

Eggs viewed from above
(rotational symmetry)

Chrysalis
(reflective symmetry)

Caterpillar
(translational symmetry)

You might use the blot pattern technique to make the butterfly.

To discuss
How objects can show a repeated pattern. Keeping and studying the life history of an insect might be a useful spin-off.

Just for fun

For children to do
1. Make *mirror people*. Fold a sheet of paper as shown.

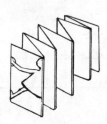

Outline and cut some *dancing dollies*. Mount them on a background to make a chorus line. It is possible to use this technique with vertical folding to make acrobats which can be hung up vertically.

2. It is not always necessary to treat the subject from the front view.

3. Make reflective portraits of yourself.

Flat   Concave   Convex

4. Make blot pattern butterflies on card, colour them, cut them out. Mount them in a *display box*. An old shirt box would be ideal.

In conclusion
Make a classroom display illustrating all the various aspects of symmetry, making it as colourful and interesting as possible.

More fun

Odd man out

Encourage the children to make *odd-man-out collections*.
Use objects or draw them as in the examples below.
Which is the odd-man-out? Remember it's all based on
symmetry.

X U
F W
O Y
M I H

Complete the symmetry.   Make symmetrical jewellery.

More to do

The Learning Through Science packs named below
contain the following cards (in addition to those mentioned
in this section), that could be adapted for use with slow
learning children.

Sky and Space
Sun and Shadow

Out of Doors
Look at Shapes
Shape and Pattern

Materials
Spoons

Moving Around
Safety Wise

ME AND MY CLOTHES

This section is intended to help children with learning difficulties to understand something of the nature of the materials that are used to clothe them. The insulating properties of fabrics, the waterproof nature of some materials and the absorbency of others; the wearing properties of clothes; the fact that dark materials absorb more heat than light ones; the readiness of some clothing to burn easily. All these and other properties of clothing are investigated in this text.

Cut out clothing outfits have been designed so that they can be photocopied for the children to colour and to clothe the boy or girl doll figures. Cutting out tabs to attach the clothes to the figures is fiddly for some children. In this case Velcro can be stuck to the clothes and to the figures. This makes for good and easy attachment. If this method is used the model figure can be left printed on a solid rectangle of card. In doing this, attention and discussion can focus on the nature of clothing that is used for different purposes. Needless to say, no science will be done until the children carry out the practical activities that accompany each set of cut out clothes.

Contents

Photocopy this page onto
heavy card and cut out.

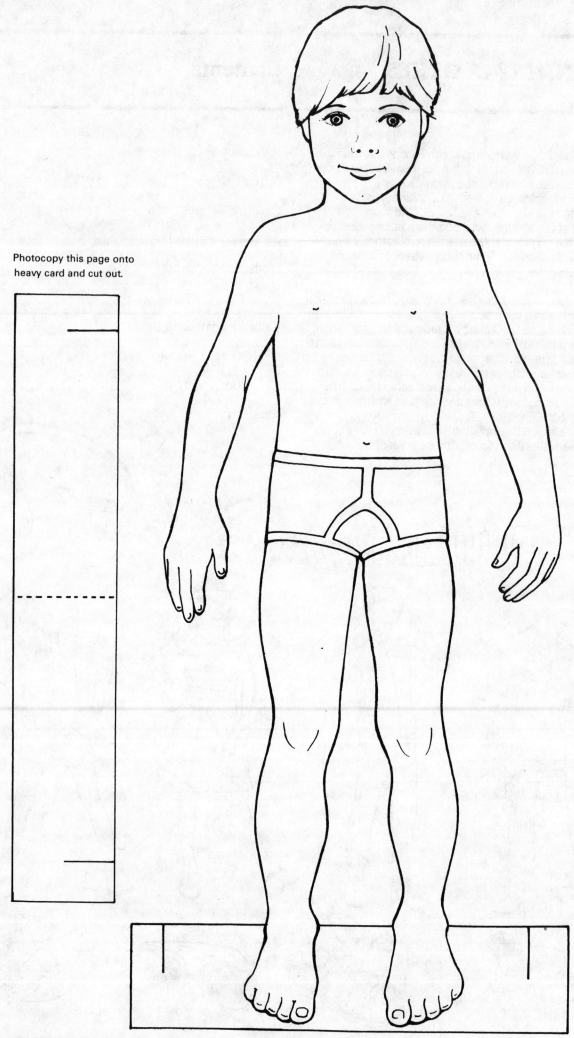

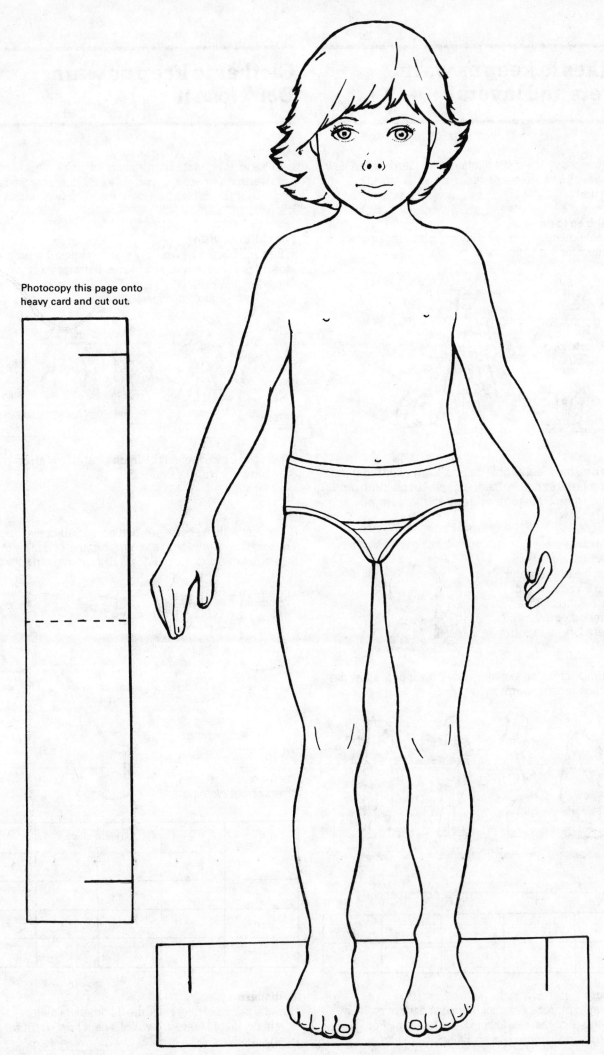

Photocopy this page onto
heavy card and cut out.

Clothes to keep us warm
Layers and layers

The nature of materials, the thickness of materials and how many layers there are of a material are all factors in keeping us warm.

For children to do

1. Wrap children up in several layers of different materials. Leave them for 5 to 10 minutes.

Discuss how they feel as time passes. If any children start to get uncomfortably hot, let them *escape*. Let children go outdoors in their *outfits* on a cold day and come in when they feel cold.

2. Talk about clothes designed to keep us warm. Establish the idea that our bodies are a *reservoir* of warmth. Let the children feel their bodies giving off heat; feel a forehead with a cool hand.

Kitchen foil held close to the face. What do you feel?

3. Encourage children to make some drawings to show the way clothes keep us warm.

The material   Thickness   Trapped air   Layers

4. Try out coats. Which is the warmest coat in school?

Name of child	Type of material	Texture	Type of padding	Zip or buttons?

To discuss

How polar explorers, Eskimos, Lapps and we ourselves keep warm. Accessories to help keep us warm. For example muffs, scarves, gloves, Balaclavas, hats.

Clothes to keep us warm
Don't lose it

In these tests hot water bottles and soft drink cans filled with warm water are set up to act as analogues of the human body. Using them children can explore how we attempt to keep warm.

For children to do

1. Beg and borrow several hot water bottles, the rubber kind. Make sure they are the same. Put warm water in each. *Dress* them in all kinds of ways. Feel them periodically throughout a couple of hours.

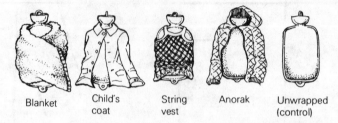

Blanket   Child's coat   String vest   Anorak   Unwrapped (control)

Which cools most quickly? Which most slowly? How do they compare with the control?

2. The test with the hot water bottles is a subjective one. Those children who can read a thermometer can try to measure rates of cooling. Fill soft drink cans with hot water.

One layer of towel   Two layers of towel   Lots of layers of thin tea towel   Unwrapped

Take the temperature every 5 minutes.

Try the same test but with layers of wet *clothing*.

		Temperature		
Time	Tin 1	Tin 2	Tin 3	Tin 4
5 min.				
10 min.				
15 min.				

To discuss

How the nature of materials, the thickness of materials and how many layers there are will all affect how warm we can keep ourselves.

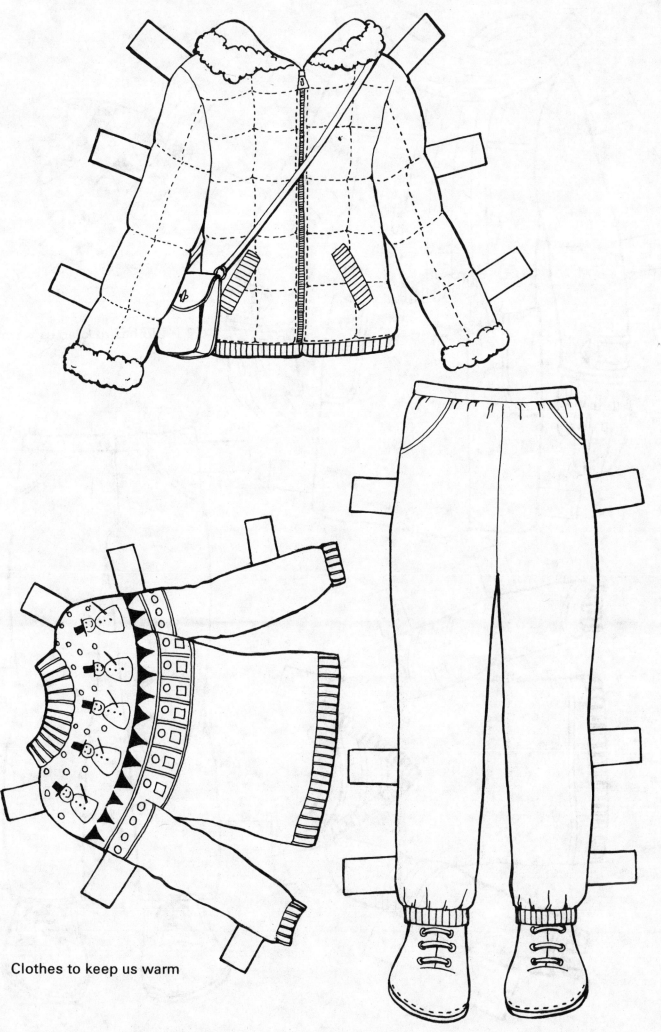

Clothes to keep us warm

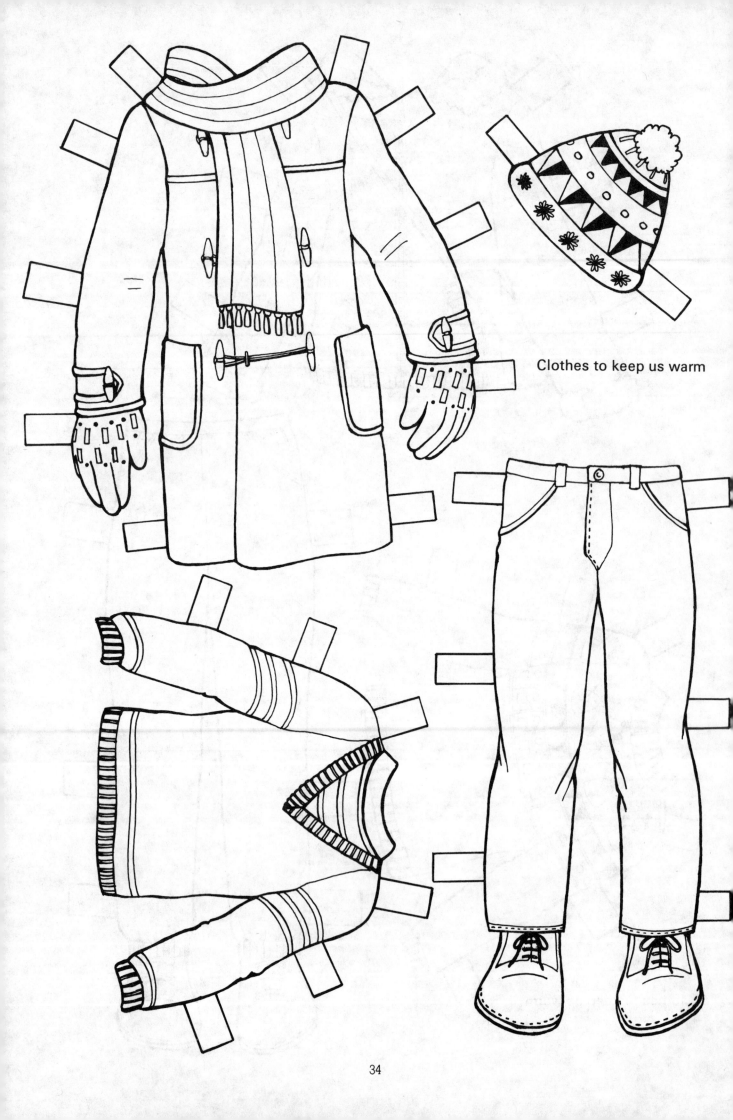

Clothes to keep us warm

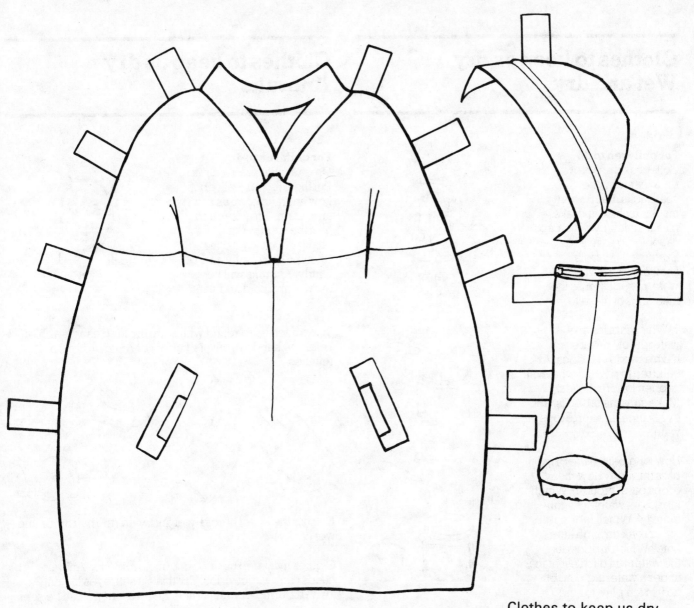

Clothes to keep us dry

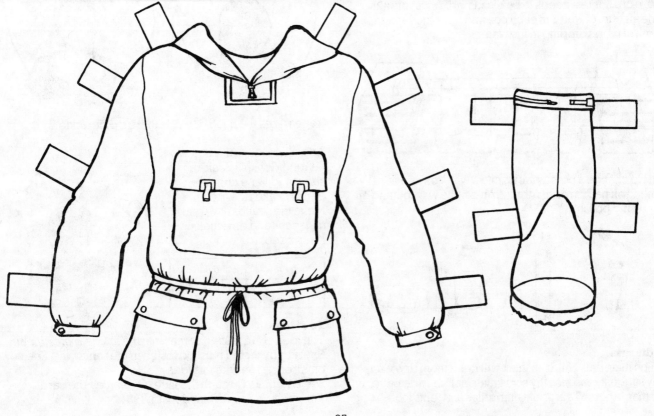

Clothes to keep us dry
Wet and dry

For children to do

Collect examples of
rainwear from the
coat-racks. Raincoats,
mackintoshes, anoraks,
plastic macs, cyclists' caps,
cagoules, gabardines.
Examine the labels:
*showerproof, rainproof,
waterproof.* Discuss the
meanings of these terms.

1. Which fabrics are
waterproof? Ensure you
have a range of fabrics. Ask
children to predict what will
happen before the test.
Make sure the fabric is taut
every time. Drip on drops of
water.

How long before the drips
pass through? How many
drops pass through? Which
fabrics let water through
quickly? Which fabrics let
water soak through after a
time? Which fabrics does
the water run off? Test macs
under a watering-can, but
do it in the playground.

2. How quickly do different fabrics soak up water? The
nature of a fair test needs to be discussed. Always put the
same amount of water in each pot, and have the same
length of fabric dipping in the water.

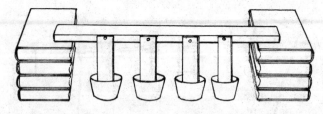

Can we change a porous fabric into a waterproof one? Try
painting on nail varnish, rubbing on candle wax, putting on
glue, using polish.

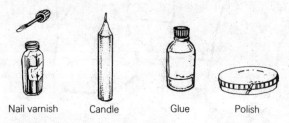

Nail varnish   Candle   Glue   Polish

To discuss

Which materials children think will keep them dry. Can
they suggest reasons why some materials may be better at
this than others? Talk about umbrellas and tents too.

Clothes to keep us dry
Anoraks

For children to do

Dress a child in an anorak.
Put the hood up. Talk about
how anoraks keep us dry
and warm. On moors and
hills the weather can
change. Quickly it can
become cold, rainy and
windy. Anoraks will keep
out wet and cold and *wind.*

Try this.
Wrap each hand round with a warm damp handkerchief.
Hold one hand in front of a hairdryer *(cold on)* for 2 or 3
minutes.

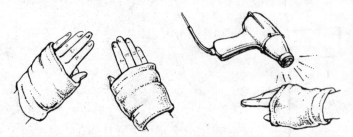

Discuss the effect of cold, wet and wind (the hairdryer and
wet hanky).

Clothes that keep us dry can bring problems. Anorak
hoods can restrict vision. Try this. Sit still, eyes looking
forward. Bring a pencil round. Record when it can be seen.

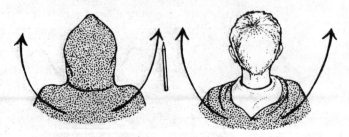

Repeat with the hood down. Is there a difference?

Anorak hoods can restrict
hearing. Try this. Make a
soft sound, for example
gently shake rice in a tin.
Make the sounds at varying
distances and directions.
Keep a record.

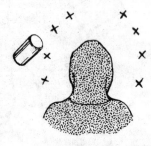

Sound made	Sound detected

To discuss

The idea of fair testing comes into the above *experiment.*
Everybody tested must be tested in the same way. See how
children get on with this idea.
See Learning Through Science, *Ourselves,* the card
Pin-pointing Sound. Macdonald, 1981.

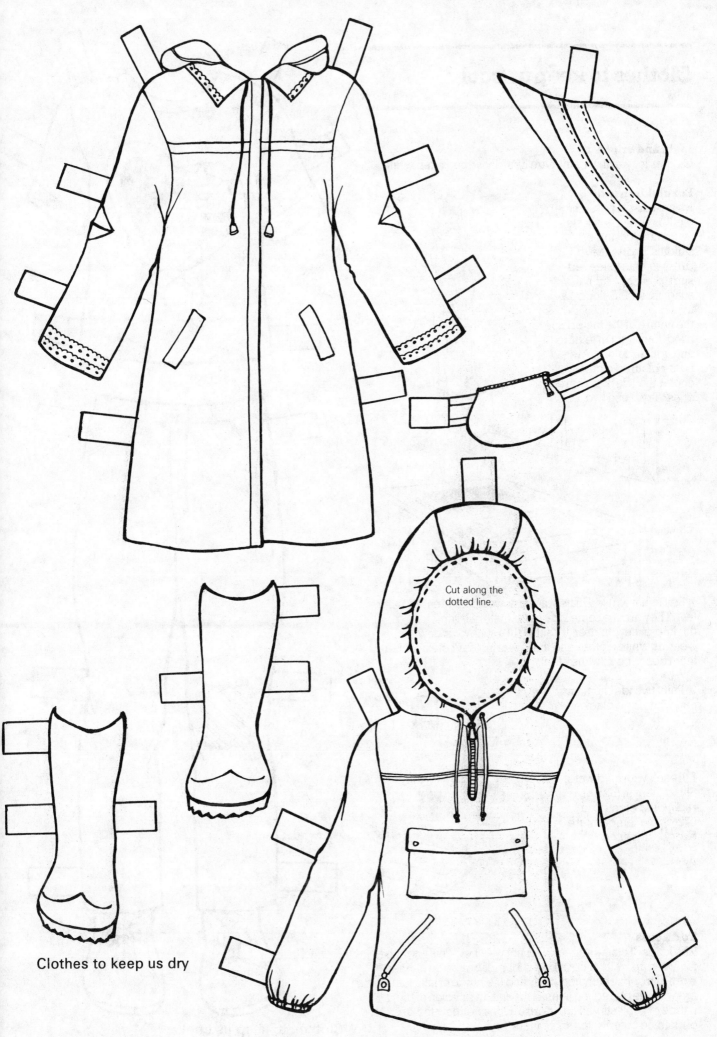

Cut along the
dotted line.

Clothes to keep us dry

37

Clothes to keep us cool

Light and bright
Clothes for warm weather are light, loose and often white.

For children to do
Make a display of summer clothes: T-shirts, shorts, swimming costumes, sandals, short-sleeved dresses, short-sleeved shirt, parasols, sunhats, sunglasses, flip-flops. Dress up a boy and a girl. Discuss the nature of the materials used: thin, light in texture and light in colour. Are light-coloured clothes cooler than dark-coloured ones? Try these two tests.

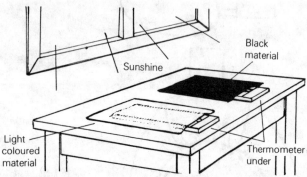

Sunshine
Black material
Light coloured material
Thermometer under

1. Felt squares used in needlework would be ideal for a fair test. They are the same size, same material, same thickness. Let children try sitting in a sunny window wearing white clothes and then wearing dark clothes. Let them describe how they feel.

2. Paint two identical tins, one white, one black.

Fill each with cold water. Stand them in front of a radiator or electric fire. Check the temperature every 10 minutes.

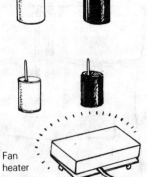

Fan heater

To discuss
The kinds of clothes needed for hot weather. This might be followed up by looking in books for pictures of the clothes worn in tropical climates, including the range of hats that are worn as protection against the sun. Discussion of the nature of fair tests will again arise. Consider how the design of clothing contributes to coolness.

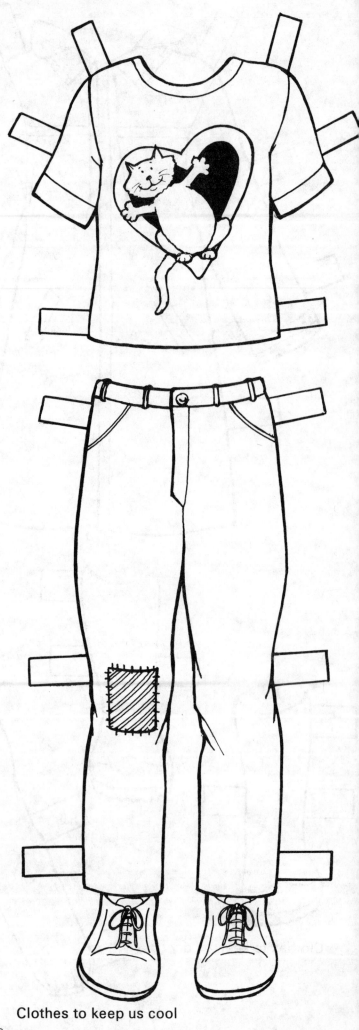

Clothes to keep us cool

Clothes to keep us cool

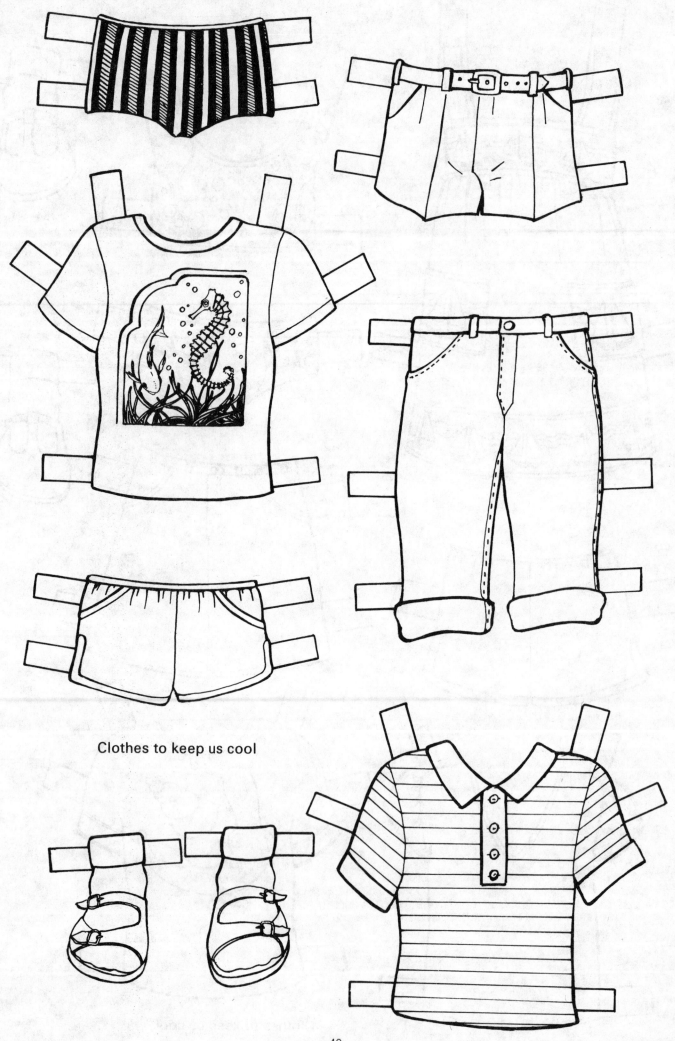

Clothes to keep us cool

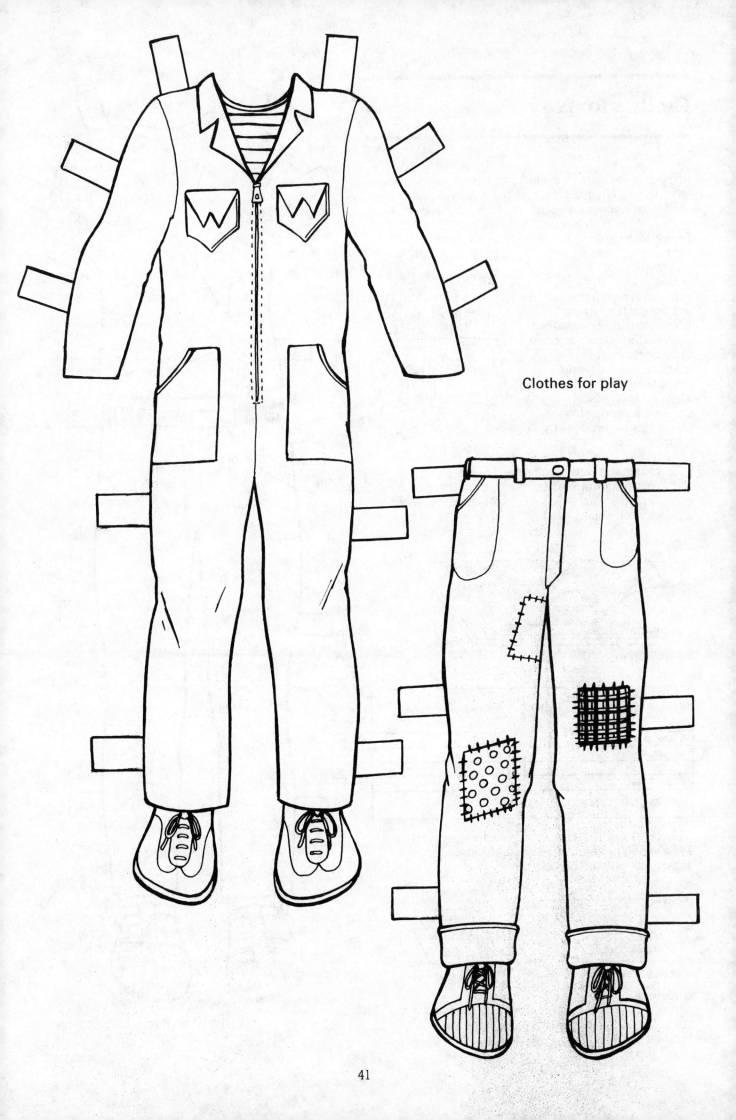

Clothes for play

41

Clothes for play

Romping and climbing, tumbling and sprawling, painting and cooking. What sort of clothes are suitable? Tough, hard-wearing ones like jeans.

For children to do

Let each child make a painting of his or her favourite outfit for playing outdoors or working indoors, at cleaning the bike or cooking. Discuss the nature of the clothes shown in the paintings, for example, jeans, overalls, dungarees, corduroys. Make a display of such clothes cut from mail order catalogues. Let children try these two tests.

my mums apron

1. How tough and hard wearing are different materials? Use relatively unworn parts of garments that have been discarded. Test samples of: jean material, overall, school uniform, work clothes.

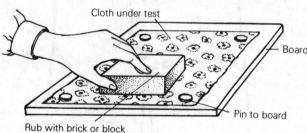

Cloth under test

Board

Pin to board

Rub with brick or block covered with sandpaper.

Examine 'new' fabric with magnifier	tape recorded comments
5 rubs, examine	
10 rubs, examine	
15 rubs, examine	
20 rubs, examine	
How many rubs to make a hole?	

2. How well do different fabrics protect from dirt and mess? Test a variety of fabrics. Examine the white paper from underneath each test piece.

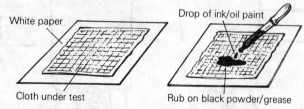

White paper

Drop of ink/oil paint

Cloth under test

Rub on black powder/grease

To discuss

Which materials are most hard wearing. Discuss also the nature of the fair test, for example, how one needs to give the same number of rubs. How one needs the same amount of *dirt* used for each test.

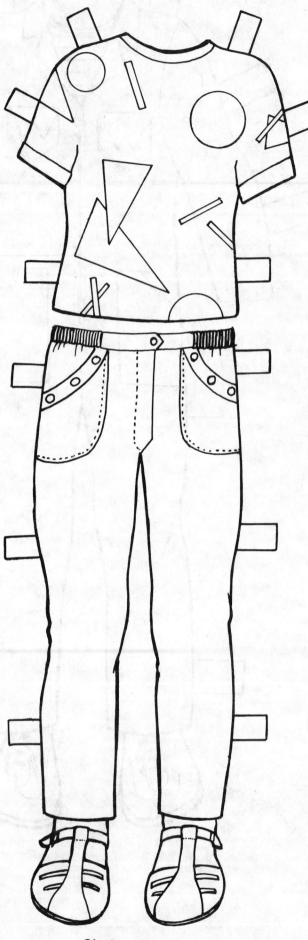

Clothes for play

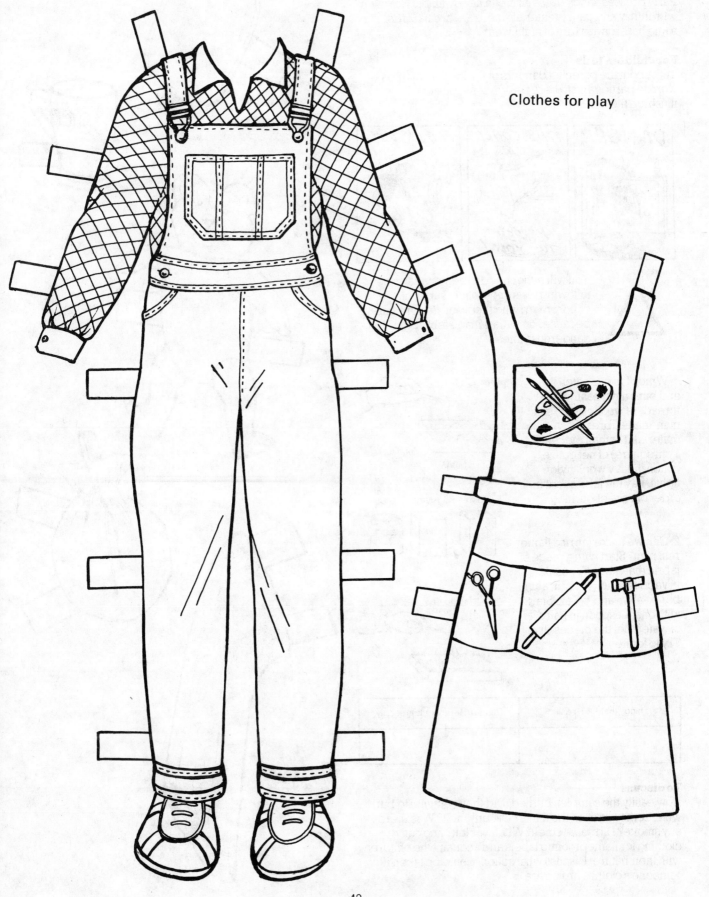

Clothes for play

Clothes for parties and for bed

Party dresses, fancy dress all mean happy times. However, with flimsy and gauzy materials there are fire hazards. The same hazards are true of night wear.

For children to do
Talk about the potential dangers of the kinds of clothes worn to parties and to bed. Design some posters to illustrate the dangers.

 You will either need to demonstrate the following tests or carefully supervise children carrying them out. Be very careful because some man-made fabrics give off dangerous fumes.

1. Which fabrics catch fire and burn most easily? Test threads of wool, cotton, silk, man-made fibres. Test materials (2 small pieces of 1 cm square) of net gauze, cotton, heavy wool, nylon tights. Lay the fabrics out in order of ease of burning.

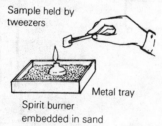

Sample held by tweezers

Metal tray

Spirit burner embedded in sand

2. Can we make fabrics flame resistant? Start with a piece of fabric that is *not*. Try soaking in various solutions: salt, alum, borax, alum and borax. Start with one teaspoon in half a jar of water. Let the pieces dry. Try to ignite.

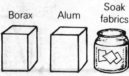

Borax   Alum   Soak fabrics

Allow fabric to dry, test again

Things that burn easily	Things that do not burn easily

To discuss
How easily the samples burned. Did they continue to burn when removed from the flame? Did any melt? Was there any smoke? Did some smell? What was left? Look at clothing for flameproofing labels and acquaint the children with their nature. Discuss what action should be taken if someone's clothes are on fire.

Clothes for bed

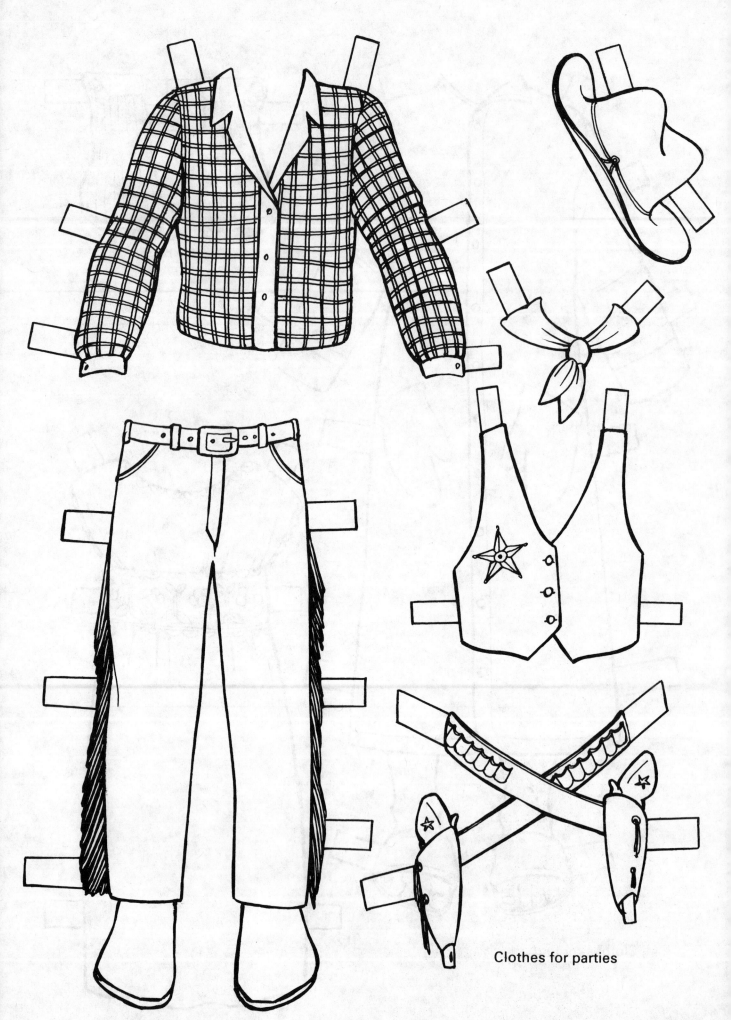

Clothes for parties

Clothes for hiding and clothes for being seen

Sometimes we do not want to be seen, like a soldier in camouflage. Sometimes we want to be seen clearly and easily like road workers in orange jackets.

For children to do

Ask the children to bring in their Action Man figures and outfits. There are quite a range. Discuss how the soldier camouflaged in khaki and green can merge with *jungle* backgrounds but would need a white outfit to *hide* in the snow. Test to find out which colours merge, which colours stand out.

Choose three backgrounds. Large sheets of sugar paper will do.

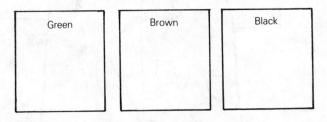

Green	Brown	Black

Choose different colours and stick them on these backgrounds.

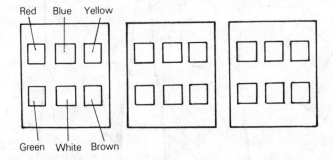

Red Blue Yellow

Green White Brown

Set up a sheet at a time right across the playground. Which colour stands out best? Which colour stands out least? Relate the findings to the colours you need to wear if you want to be seen: in fields and grass; against soil and rocks; in the night.

To discuss

Camouflage in animals. The need to be still when camouflaged. Camouflage the cut out clothes and try *hiding* your cut out figure.

See Learning Through Science, *Colour*, the card *Being Seen and Hiding*, Macdonald, 1981.

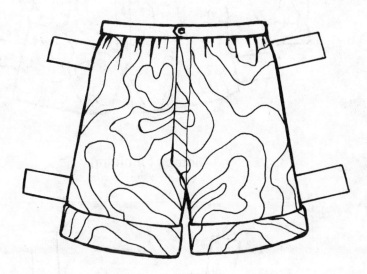

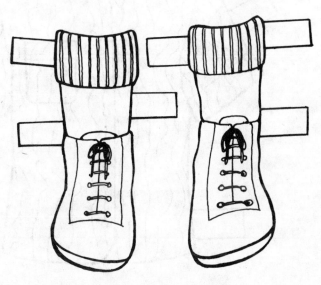

Clothes for hiding

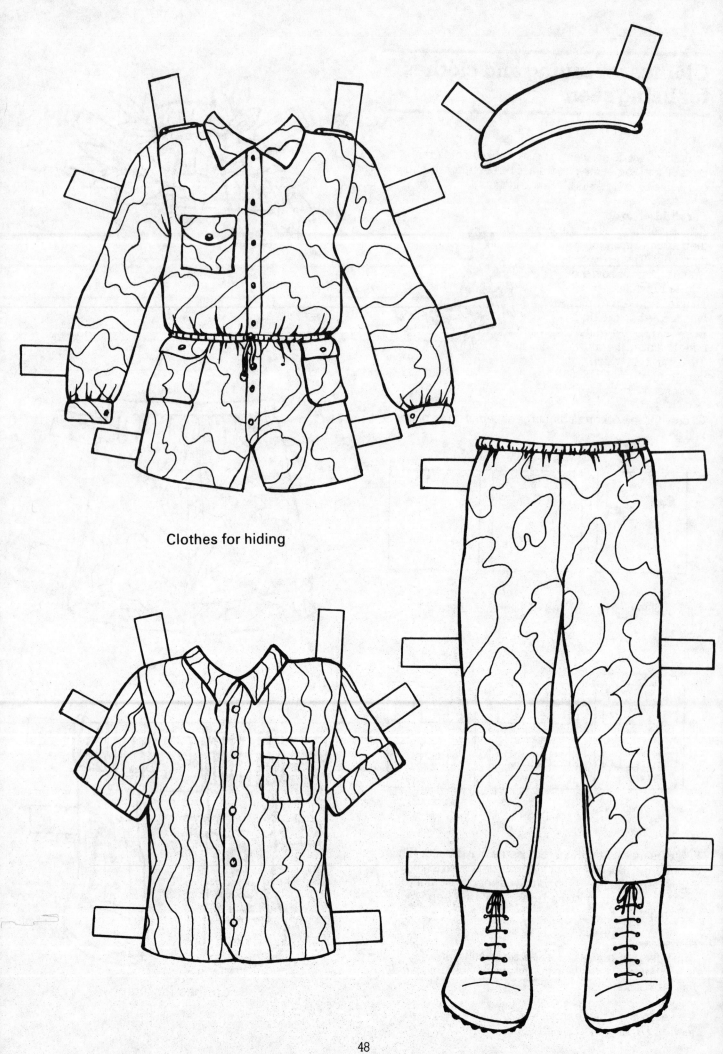

Clothes for hiding

Clothes for an astronaut

Children are fascinated and knowledgeable about space and spacemen. The astronaut's outfit, designed as it is to protect him from heat and radiation, is of particular interest.

For children to do
Make a spaceman cut out. Arrange it in different positions around the spaceship.

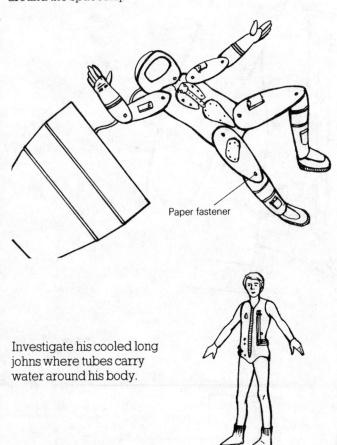

Paper fastener

Investigate his cooled long johns where tubes carry water around his body.

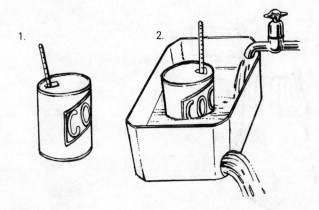

Fill two soft drink cans with warm water. Put (2) in a plastic container that has a hole in the base. Put cold water through. Which tin cools more quickly?

1.

2.

To discuss
How running water can conduct heat away. Hence astronauts can be kept cool.

Apollo spacesuit assembly.

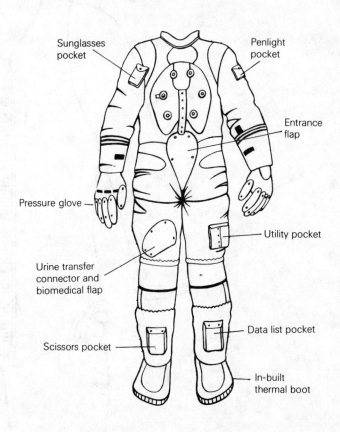

Sunglasses pocket

Penlight pocket

Entrance flap

Pressure glove

Utility pocket

Urine transfer connector and biomedical flap

Data list pocket

Scissors pocket

In-built thermal boot

Liquid-cooling garment worn beneath EVA spacesuit.

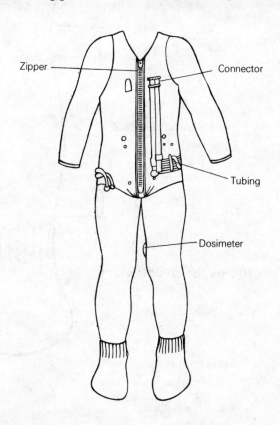

Zipper

Connector

Tubing

Dosimeter

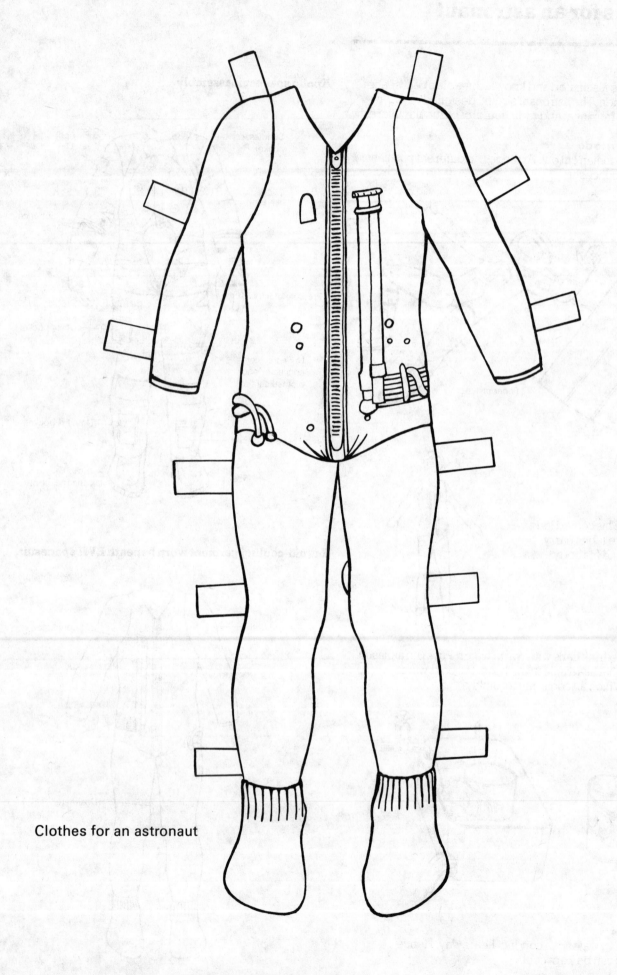

Clothes for an astronaut

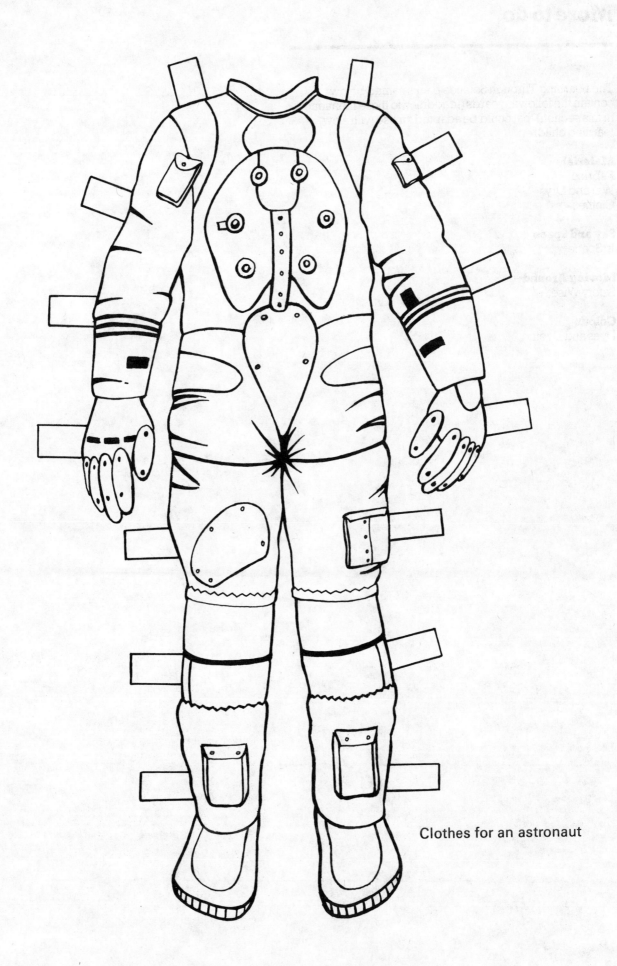

Clothes for an astronaut

More to do

The Learning Through Science packs named below
contain the following cards (in addition to those mentioned
in this section) that could be adapted for use with slow
learning children.

Materials
Fabrics
Wet and Dry
Clothes

Sky and Space
In Space

Moving Around
Safety Wise

Colour
Dyes and Dyeing

ME AND OTHER GROWING THINGS

Contents

This section is intended to help children with learning difficulties to understand the meaning of *growth* in themselves, in other living things, and in some other ways. The *Concise Oxford Dictionary* defines the noun as 'growing, development, increase in size or value'. The work introduces children to some changes brought about by growth, and enables them to find growth patterns. Most of the activities suggested only take a short time.

Me growing

All children are conscious that they increase in height and change in other ways as the years pass. The following will help them look more closely at these aspects of growth.

For children to do
Collect baby pictures of the children in the group. Mount them as a group montage. Number each photograph. Guess who each one is. Record the results.

Name	Picture 1	Picture 2	Picture 3	etc.
John	Andrew	John	Mary	
Ray	Andrew	Peter	Mary	
Peter	Andrew	John	Ann	
Ann	Andrew	Paul	Mary	

Why are some people easier to guess than others? (Probably because some characteristic feature persists.) What changes have occurred, for instance growth of hair, increase in height, increase in girth, bigger feet, bigger everything? Does the head seem large in the baby photographs? Compare children in other classes with the children in the group. Take younger and older classes. Look at head size, height, weight, hand span, foot length and so on. See *Me and my Friends* on page 9.

To discuss
There is much to discuss about the changes that occur. If it is difficult getting baby pictures of the group, then any baby pictures cut from magazines and from other sources will help. The large size of the head in babies and the relatively small increase in size of it in relation to the increase in size of the whole body are worth dwelling on. Outgrown clothes and shoes, articles children used as a baby and so on help emphasise the comparison with their previous size.

Growth patterns

The following suggestions take up relationships between height and other factors such as length of stride. Looking for pattern in this way is an important scientific process to develop with children.

For children to do
Ask the children to measure the height of each person in the group. A tape pinned on the wall is a good aid to use. Paper pinned to the wall can be marked directly.

Name	Height

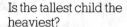

Is the tallest child the heaviest?

Does the tallest child have the widest arm span? Make marks on a sheet pinned to the wall. Strips of paper cut to the height, arm span and length of stride may help when comparisons are made. Use a different colour for each child.

Is the tallest child the one with the biggest stride?

To discuss
Relationships between height, weight, length of stride and arm span.
See Learning Through Science, *Ourselves*, Macdonald, 1981.

Reach for the sky

Human growth is easy to measure, but it is a long-term exercise. Here is an exercise giving quick results.

For children to do
Line up the group in order of height. Mark the increase in height as you go from person to person.

Ask each child to reach up with arms stretched. Keep the feet flat on the ground. Mark where they reach to.

Some schools found it useful to mark the height of each child with a strip of paper stuck on the wall. This could be topped with a self portrait.

To discuss
It should be possible to see a relationship between the children's height line and their reach line. That is to say, each line will be at about the same angle to the horizontal. As we grow our ability to reach grows with us but is in direct relationship to our height. Many children with learning difficulties may find it hard to put this into words, but the activity will probably give them a *feel* for the relationship.

See Learning Through Science, *Ourselves*, Macdonald, 1981.

Seed sorts

There is an enormous variety of seeds. A good start can be made by collecting, sorting and displaying a range of seeds.

For children to do
Collect a variety of seeds: apple, melon, rice, pomegranate, date, broom, lupin, sycamore, sunflower. Hamster food and commercial bird seed mixtures are a good source. Talk about the shapes and colours, textures and sizes. Sort and separate them and make patterns and pictures.

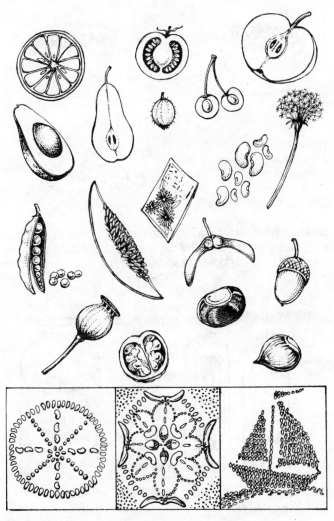

To discuss
Talk about the different sizes of seeds, feel the varying textures, look at the colours, discuss the different shapes. Sort the seeds according to their size, their colour, and whether they are rough or smooth. Which are the children familiar with? Which grow in the garden? Which grow in the wild? Which were inside fleshy structures, such as apple, tomato or melon? Which were inside dry seed cases, like lupin or poppy? Be careful to distinguish between the seed case (the fruit) and the seed or seeds inside.

Learning Through Science, *All Around*, the card *Investigate a Plant 2*, Macdonald, 1982.

Growing ways

Plants are much too static to keep children with learning difficulties interested for long and it is helpful to take some quick growing plants such as mustard or cress to study germination.

For children to do
Quick growers
Sow some mustard or cress in good loamy soil or a seed compost. Space the seeds well. Cover them with a very light sprinkling of soil, and water gently. In one pot sow the seeds very densely. Note the competition that occurs.

Slow Growers
Soak some bean seeds overnight.

Discuss why they swell.

Does it matter which way you plant them? Put them next to the glass in a large jar full of damp sand or sawdust, or grow them in a squeezy bottle as shown.

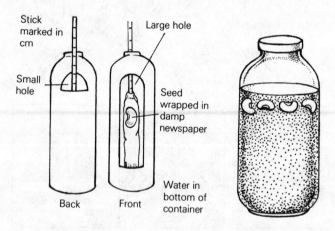

Stick marked in cm

Small hole

Large hole

Seed wrapped in damp newspaper

Water in bottom of container

Back   Front

Will half a bean seed grow? Soak the seeds before you cut them.

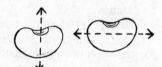

Discuss
How the mustard or cress seedlings grow. Pull a few up each day and look at the parts beneath the soil. Discuss competition amongst the densely sown seedlings for light and air and water. The fact that roots always appear before shoots, to take up water and to anchor the plant, and that roots always eventually grow downwards and shoots upwards.

Seed needs

For children to do
Most children think seeds need soil to germinate. Try them on the different media shown here. Try them on damp orange peel, cardboard and sponge too. Use mustard or cress seeds again. Remember to watch that the children keep them damp and not wet. How long will the seedlings continue to grow on these media.

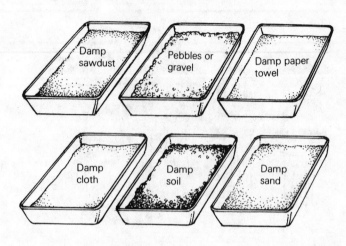

Damp sawdust   Pebbles or gravel   Damp paper towel

Damp cloth   Damp soil   Damp sand

Is light or darkness needed for germination?

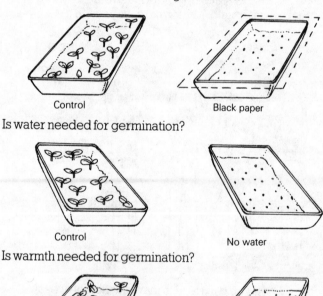

Control   Black paper

Is water needed for germination?

Control   No water

Is warmth needed for germination?

Control   Put in refrigerator

The control container has all possible requirements each time.

To discuss
How seeds will germinate on many media, but that they need light, water and warmth. Grow some seedlings in a cupboard to see what happens to the plants in the absence of light.

Seedling growth

For children to do

1. Does it matter how deeply seeds are sown? Cut the tops from three transparent plastic squash bottles. Make drainage holes in the bottom.

1. Seeds 2 cm from bottom

2. Seeds in middle

3. Seeds 1 cm deep

If possible use wheat, barley or sweet-corn seeds. Put 20 seeds in each bottle. Make sure that some fall near the edge, so their growth can be watched. Cover the jars with removable sleeves of sugar paper. Keep the soil damp. Watch how the seeds grow. Every day record the numbers which have emerged from the soil. Try other kinds of seed.

Day	Jar 1	Jar 2	Jar 3
1			
2			
3			

2. Seeds can be weight lifters, how strong are they? Cut some pieces of polystyrene ceiling tile to fit inside 250 g cottage cheese cartons. Sow 10 pea seeds in soil in each carton. Put the seeds about 1 cm deep. Water well. Put a disc of polystyrene, then a mass on top of the soil in each carton. Which masses do the children think the seeds will lift? Keep the soil watered and watch what happens. Try other seeds and different masses.

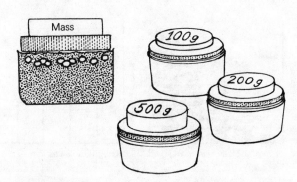

To discuss

1. The depth at which seeds are normally sown, between one and two times their diameter. Seeds normally contain rather more food than the seedlings need, but not enough to sustain growth through several centimetres of soil. Think about wild plants. How deeply is their seed covered?

2. Discuss the masses plants can lift. Have children seen pavements and roads lifted by the roots of plants?

One plant

For children to do

Let each child in the group dig up *one* common plant growing around the school, for example any weed or bedding plant such as a geranium or wallflower which has finished flowering. Do it carefully. Wash the roots gently. Spread it out and make a careful drawing onto centimetre squared paper. Draw it full size.

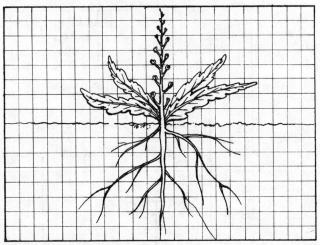

To discuss

Whilst the children are drawing, talk about the things they can see. Ask the sorts of questions outlined below.

Stems	Leaves	Flowers and seed pads	Roots
Do they branch?	Where are youngest?	Where?	Colour?
Colour?	Shape?	Colour?	Do they branch?
All over?	Any veins?	Pattern of petals?	Always the same thickness?
Shape?	What pattern?	How are flowers arranged?	Feel the roots: Are they soft and slimy?
Square, round, ridged?	What is leaf edge like?		Stiff and wiry?
Hairy?	Are leaves stalked?		Hard and woody?
	Hairy?		
	What colour is leaf? On top? Underneath?		
	Are they arranged: in pairs? alternately? spirally?		

See Learning Through Science, *All Around*, the card *Investigate a Plant 1*, and *Out of Doors*, the cards *Look at Shape* (Leaf Shapes), *How Many?* (Search for Patterns in Leaves) and *Good Guesses* (How Many Leaves), Macdonald, 1982.

Plant sizes

A walk around the school should yield several plants varying in height. Dig them up carefully. Include a grass in your collection. Plot their height and depth on centimetre squared paper. It may be easiest for children to do this full size.

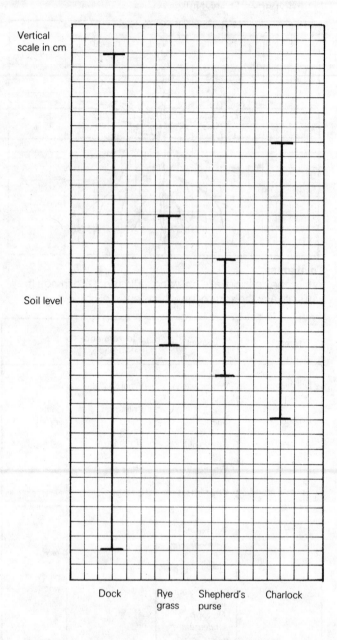

Vertical scale in cm

Soil level

Dock   Rye grass   Shepherd's purse   Charlock

To discuss
How some plants have deeper rooting systems than others. How some plants grow higher than others. This enables plants to live, often quite densely, in a community where they can between them make maximum use of the light, air and whole depth of the top soil layer. Look at the layering in woodland where there are four distinct zones. The ground flora such as mosses and liverworts, the herb layer of plants such as bracken and bluebell, the shrub layer and the tree layer.

Little and large – leaves

Two very common plants that show interesting patterns in their leaf growth are the dandelion and the privet.

For children to do
1. Collect dandelion leaves from a number of plants. Try and find plants growing in different places, for example a mown lawn, the shade of a hedge, a neglected grassy patch, cracks at the base of walls. Draw round the leaves, or mount them under transparent sticky backed plastic.

2. Collect about 100 privet twigs. Pluck the leaves from the twigs and sort them into groups according to size. Carefully measure the length of each leaf on a ruler marked at 5 mm intervals. Make groups of leaves 10-15 mm long, 15-20 mm long, 20-25 mm long and so on. Count the leaves in each group. Make a block graph if the children can understand, or use the leaves to make the graph.

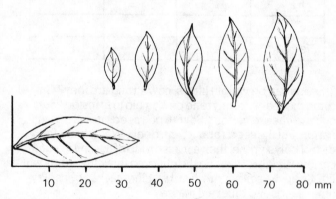

10   20   30   40   50   60   70   80   mm

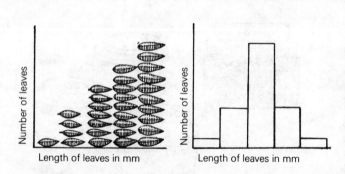

Number of leaves

Length of leaves in mm   Length of leaves in mm

To discuss
How the difference in length of dandelion leaves is probably related to the difference in environmental conditions, the biggest leaves growing in moist and shady conditions. How the biggest group of privet leaves is about in the middle of the size range, and there are fewer smaller and larger leaves.

See Learning Through Science, *Out of Doors*, the card *How Big?*, Macdonald, 1982.

Watching roots grow

For children to do

Put some cuttings into water and watch the roots develop. Use fuchsia, busy lizzy (Impatiens balsamina), coleus or tradescantia. Choose young shoots. Cut below leaves with a sharp knife or scissors. Cut off the lower leaves flush with the stem. Pinch out flower buds and stand the shoot in a bottle full of water in bright light.

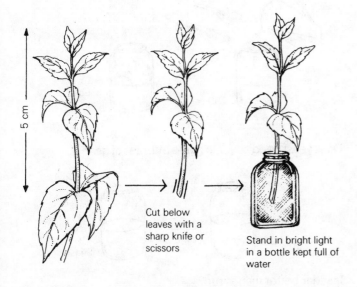

5 cm

Cut below leaves with a sharp knife or scissors

Stand in bright light in a bottle kept full of water

Twigs of poplar and willow also root very easily in water. Stand them in tall jars.

Cuttings are often slow to root from October to February. During these months it might be better to watch roots develop from onions or bulbs such as hyacinth or daffodil, balanced on top of jars of water, and kept in good light.

Water kept just below base of bulb. Place jar in good light.

To discuss

When do the children notice the first root? Where does it grow from? What colour are the roots, how do they branch? What do they feel and smell like? Will the new plant keep on growing in water? Transfer it to a larger jar when it has a lot of roots. See how long it survives. Add fertilizer such as Baby Bio to the water of some. Does this help?

Grow some

There is a lot to be observed as plants grow.

For the children to do

Grow potatoes

Find an old plastic bucket. Make plenty of holes in the bottom with a metal rod or an old screwdriver. Alternatively use a twelve inch plant pot. Use Levington compost or half peat half garden soil and an *old* potato the size of a hen's egg. Fill the pot or bucket two thirds full with compost. Plant the potato about 5 cm deep. Stand on wooden slats in a good light and keep damp. As the shoots grow add more compost until the pot is full. Keep the lower stems buried, but not the leaves.

Plastic bucket

12″ pot

Grow Wheat

Again use an old plastic bucket or a twelve inch pot. Use John Innes No. 2 compost or another soil based compost. Scatter wheat seeds thinly, about 1 cm apart. Cover with 1 cm compost. Stand on wooden slats in a light place. Keep damp.

To discuss

Draw the children's attention to the growth of the plants from time to time. A record of increase in height can be made on a marker placed in the pots. Discuss other changes apart from increase in height. Harvest the crops. Eat the potatoes. Make flour from the wheat grains, add more flour to it and make some bread.

Tallest plant

See *Growing Yeast* on page 60.

Growing bean sprouts

Buy some mung* beans.

For children to do
Put a small teaspoonful of beans into an 8 oz cottage cheese carton. Cover with cold water. Put the lid on the carton. Next day pour off the water, replace the lid without adding more water. Keep at room temperature not in the sun or over a radiator. Every morning add fresh water, rinse the seeds, pour off the water. In a warm room the sprouts will be big enough to eat in 4 or 5 days.

1. Put beans in carton

2. Cover with water

3. Put lid on carton

5. Replace lid

4. Next day pour off water

6. Everyday rinse seeds, pour off water

Have a bean sprout competition. On Monday morning give each child five beans to grow. On Friday afternoon find who has the largest and who the shortest. The sprouts will not be straight. One way of measuring them would be to use a piece of string. Do the biggest seeds make the largest sprouts?

Sprout some other seeds: black eyed beans, aduki beans, haricot beans, fenugreek, soya beans, chickpeas. What difference do the children notice? Do they all taste the same? Does their taste vary with age?

 Do not use any red kidney beans. These are poisonous unless they are well boiled.

How do the seeds grow if they are sown in soil? What sort of plants develop?

*Mung beans and many other seeds for sprouting may be bought from Messrs Thompson & Morgan (Ipswich Ltd), London Road, Ipswich, Suffolk, IP2 0BA.

Growing yeast

Yeast is a living organism which feeds on sugar and produces carbon dioxide gas as it grows.

For the children to do
Watch yeast make bubbles of gas. Put one teaspoonful of dried yeast and one teaspoonful of sugar in 200 cc of water at about 30°C. Stir well. Keep warm for 10-15 minutes.

Warm water (30°C)   200 cc   Dried yeast   Sugar   Froth of bubbles of gas

Does yeast need sugar to make bubbles of gas?

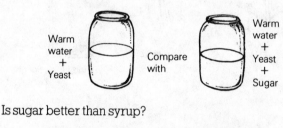

Warm water + Yeast   Compare with   Warm water + Yeast + Sugar

Is sugar better than syrup?

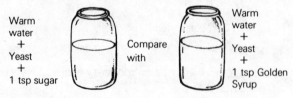

Warm water + Yeast + 1 tsp sugar   Compare with   Warm water + Yeast + 1 tsp Golden Syrup

Does the temperature matter?

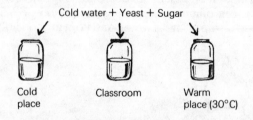

Cold water + Yeast + Sugar

Cold place   Classroom   Warm place (30°C)

Make some bread. Add 1 level teaspoon of sugar and 1 level teaspoon of dried yeast to 150 cc of warm water. Leave until frothy. Mix 225 g of flour with 1 teaspoon of salt, rub in 25 g of lard. Pour in the frothy yeast, mix and knead well. Make into 8 rolls. Put them on a greased tray in a warm place until they have doubled in size. Bake for about 20 minutes in a hot oven. Try making some bread without yeast.

To discuss
That very small organisms also grow and need food and suitable conditions to do so.

Growing crystals 1

For children to do

1. Make some crystals.

Stir into cold water as much salt as will dissolve. Put one tablespoon of the liquid into a saucer and leave overnight in a warm place.

Salt

Cold water
Stir in as much salt
as will dissolve

1 tablespoon

Leave overnight
in a warm place

Crystals of salt

Make other crystals in the same way. Try sugar, Epsom salts, bath salts, health salts. Look at them with a hand lens. Are they all the same shape?

Who can make the biggest crystals? Try making them in a warm and cold place. Try using different strengths of solution.

2. Watch crystals growing.

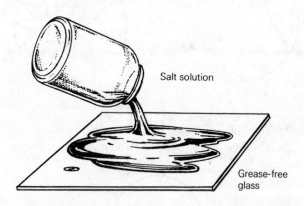

Salt solution

Grease-free
glass

Make a thin film of salt solution on a *clean* piece of glass or microscope slide. Make sure the glass is free from grease otherwise the film will not spread properly. It is best to wash the glass thoroughly with detergent and then to rinse it well. Put onto a dark background in a warm place. Watch with a hand lens or binocular microscope. Try other household substances. Which form crystals?

Growing crystals 2

For children to do

Grow large crystals

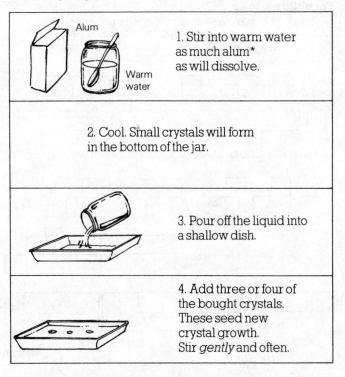

Alum

Warm
water

1. Stir into warm water as much alum* as will dissolve.

2. Cool. Small crystals will form in the bottom of the jar.

3. Pour off the liquid into a shallow dish.

4. Add three or four of the bought crystals. These seed new crystal growth. Stir *gently* and often.

5. At the end of the day take out the best crystals, dry them on blotting paper and keep them overnight.

6. Next day make a new solution, as in step 1.

7. Cool, and pour off the liquid into a shallow dish, as step 3.

8. *Seed* with the large crystals you made yesterday and stir, as step 4.

9. Dry large crystals on blotting paper. Store in an airtight box.

For copper sulphate* crystals use glass containers and allow 2 or 3 days for steps 4 and 7.

This compound is poisonous.

To grow crystals of photographer's *hypo* (sodium thiosulphate*) dissolve 4 tablespoonfuls of the substance in 1 tablespoonful of cold water, then continue from step 3. These crystals must be kept in an airtight box, otherwise they will disintegrate.

*From your local secondary school or chemist.

61

Numbers growing

Children often appreciate patterns in number growth if they are presented in some geometrical form.

For children to do
Let each child have a strip of centimetre square paper which is 15 cm long x 1 cm wide. Cut off 1, 2, 3, 4 and 5 squares in sequence.

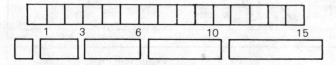

Re-arranging the strips will show more about this sequence.

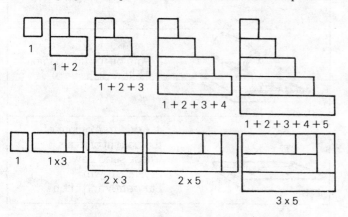

Hundred squares also show number growth. Let the children make some number lines from 1 to a 100. This one shows multiples of 3. Other multiples can be shown.

Break each line into tens and re-arrange it to make a 100 square. Do this for all multiples up to 10. Use different colours for each multiple.

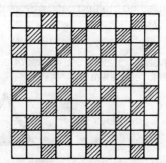

To discuss
Some children may well be able to overtly discuss the way the numbers grow. Others may only be able to get a covert feeling for what is happening. Choose other sets of strips to give other number sequences.

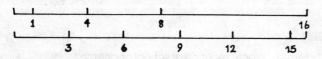

Going round in circles

Use a Spirograph to make some patterns. Look at the numbers on the wheels and the rings. Does this help children decide on the number of loops in the pattern?

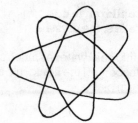

Here is another way to show how as numbers grow they make new patterns. Make a sheet of circles with 12 points.

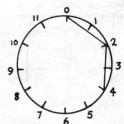

Starting to make the multiple of 2.

For children to do
Draw multiples of 2, 3, 4 up to 11.

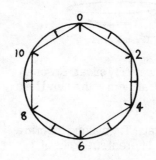
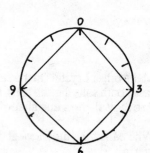
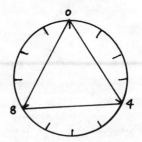
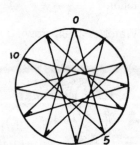

What do children notice about the patterns?
Which multiples use all the points?
Try it with further circles with different numbers of points.

To discuss
Why children get the various shapes and patterns each time. See also Learning Through Science, *Time, Growth and Change*, Macdonald, 1984.

ME AND OTHER THINGS THAT MOVE

Contents

This section introduces children with learning difficulties to some aspects of movement, ranging from the movement of their own bodies to the number of ways in which man helps the movement of people and objects. It gives childen experiences which, later, will help them to understand the concept of energy.

How fast?

For children to do

1. Mark a measured distance of 50 m. Which child will be the fastest walker? Which the slowest? Guess the order of walking speed. Now test. Keep a record. The rule for walking in sports states a walk is a heel-to-toe action, there must be unbroken contact with the ground. Anything else is on the way to running and does not count.

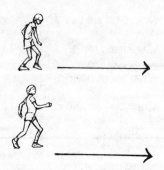

Name	Guessed fastest walker	Time	Actual order

2. Is the fastest walker also the fastest runner? Use the same measured distance to find out. Some children might guess the time. Keep a record.

Name	Guessed winner	Time	Order

3. Put the children in order of height. Is there a pattern between height and walking and running time?

To discuss

Any patterns that emerge between height and ability to walk or run well. Sometimes there may not be a pattern, but it is just as important to discover this as to find there is a relationship. You can also discuss the changes that occur after running. The heart beats faster, breathing rate increases and one often feels hotter.

Where do we bend?

We have a skeleton to hold us up and together, and muscles to pull on the bones so that we can bend at the joints.

For children to do

1. Take the children to the hall or a large open space. Let them pretend they are floppy without a skeleton rather like a rag doll. Talk about how we need bones to hold us up.

2. Now tell them they have a skeleton, but it is only jointed at the shoulders and hips. Ask them to walk about rather as robots would, stiff-limbed.

3. Let the children draw round one another onto large sheets of paper with a felt pen. Newspaper will do.

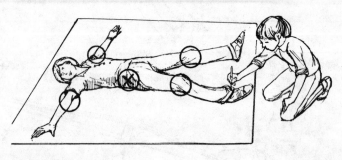

Mark every joint with a circle. How many can children find?

To discuss

The many complicated movements we make. How we need a jointed body to move. How some joints bend in only one direction (hinge joints). Leave these marked with an empty circle. How some joints move in all directions (ball and socket joints). Put a cross inside the circle. Collect bones, ending in different kinds of joints, from chickens or the Sunday joint.

Make a moveable man

Copy the shapes on this page on to stiff card. Cut out the pieces, punch out the circles and assemble with paper fasteners.

The joints should be quite stiff. One way to stop them from slipping is to stick linen reinforcing circles round the holes before the paper fasteners are put in. Gently tap both sides of each fastener with a hammer.

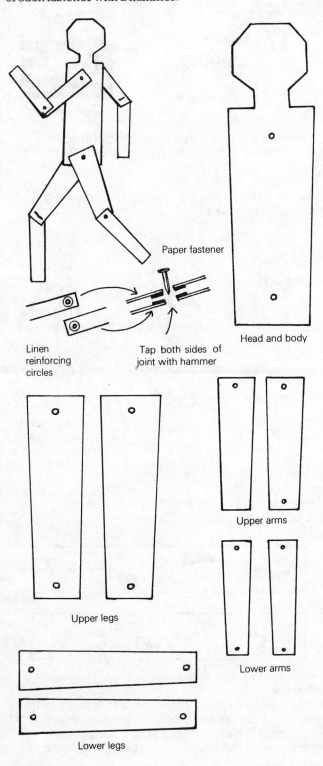

Paper fastener

Linen reinforcing circles

Tap both sides of joint with hammer

Head and body

Upper arms

Upper legs

Lower arms

Lower legs

What sequence?

Encourage the children to watch *how* we move.

For children to do
Let the children watch someone moving *slowly* in front of them. Watch several times, talk about the sequence of movements. Let the children try to copy the demonstrator with their model (left). The demonstrator should frequently freeze.

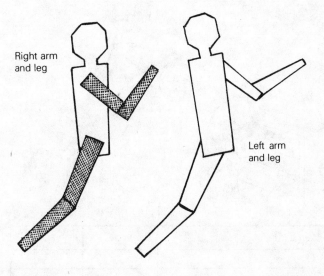

Right arm and leg

Left arm and leg

Now ask them to try to draw the movements.

It will be easier if the demonstrator has his left arm and leg clearly indicated by a colour. Try using old coloured tights or stockings, or coloured PE bands. The children could use the same colour to draw them; and the right arm and leg could be indicated by and drawn in a different colour.

The children's drawings may be crude but persevere, for they will get quite a good idea of sequence.

To discuss
How the body is constantly moved, yet kept upright with the main mass always roughly in the centre. This is necessary for keeping a balance.

More pushes and pulls

The movements we make are all either pushes or pulls. Twists are both pushes *and* pulls.

For children to do

1. Ask the children to think about the things they do. Decide which involve pushes, which involve pulls. Try them out if they cannot decide. Find examples of each in school and at home. Keep a record.

What I did	Push	Pull
Lift pencil		
Write		
Moved a window up		

2. How hard can you push or pull? Push as hard as you can against bathroom scales propped on a shelf. Pull as hard as you can. Make a record.

Name	Push	Pull

To discuss

Pushing and pulling as hard as we can involves arms, legs and body, so weight helps muscle strength. Is there any clear relationship between the best pushers and pullers, their weight, and their height?

Footprints

When we move we can leave a trail. This can tell us more about the way we move.

For children to do

Encourage the children to make footprints.

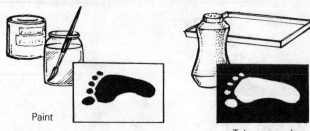

Paint

Talcum powder

1. Paint a foot with powder paint and press it on white paper. Put some talcum powder in a tray, dip a foot into it and press it on black paper.

2. Make some footprints: standing upright; crouching to leap; standing on one leg.

Standing upright

Crouching

Standing on one leg

3. Use kitchen paper to record *walking* and *running* footprints. Try hopping, jumping and skipping.

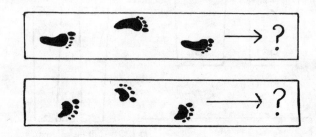

To discuss

Whether children can work out from the prints where they pushed hard. The spread of the powder paint usually shows clearly where the forces were applied. Look at how the toes are used, and discuss the differences between moving and still prints.

Stretch it

These stretchers measure the pull of the earth on certain masses.

For children to do
Many packaging materials are thrown away. Treated imaginatively, we can re-cycle them and get some good science.

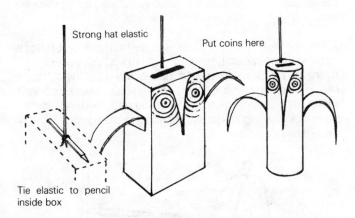

Strong hat elastic

Put coins here

Tie elastic to pencil inside box

Take 5p pieces or metal washers about 2 cm diameter. Add them one at a time to the stretcher. Mark a sheet of paper fixed alongside as you do so.

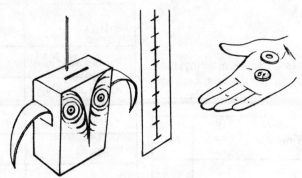

Take 10p pieces or thick metal washers about 2.5 cm diameter. Add them one at a time to the stretcher. Mark a sheet of paper fixed alongside as you do so.

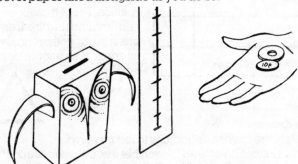

Put in an unknown number of coins. Can the stretcher tell how many?

To discuss
The relationship between the number of coins added and the stretch in the elastic. Try it with other coins too. Try it with marbles.

Moving me by carrying and dragging

Actually moving someone will help children to understand the concepts involved in moving a load.

For children to do
1. Can children carry a friend pick-a-back? Is this easy? How far can they get? Mark out a line to try along. The weight of the load might be important.

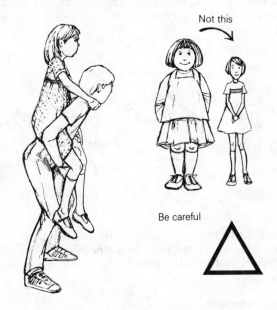

Not this

Be careful

John carried Jim 30 m	Jim weighs?
Jim carried John 19 m	John weighs?

2. Get children to try dragging each other on a mat. Drag over different surfaces: carpet, polished wood, tiles, grass. Which is the easiest surface. Is this easier than carrying?

To discuss
Whether dragging is easier than carrying. Whether the Indian travois method is easier than a flat sledge.

Moving me by rollers and wheels

For children to do

1. Find a large carton from the supermarket, one that children can easily get into. Let the children try moving each other in this way. (You might also use a small upturned table.) Use rollers such as cricket stumps, cut broom handles, dowel rods, old stair rods. Children will have to form a relay team to transfer rollers from the rear to the front as the box is pulled along. How easy is it to move a child in this way?

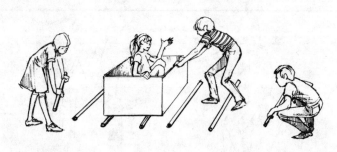

2. This is the most sophisticated one to try but worth persevering with. It is a fiddle to get the marbles into the tin lids, but you will finish up with a trolley that is very easy to move.

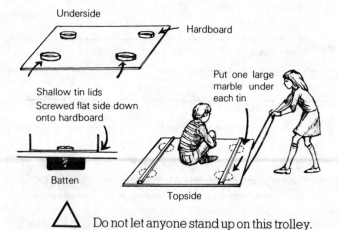

Underside

Hardboard

Shallow tin lids
Screwed flat side down
onto hardboard

Batten

Put one large marble under each tin

Topside

⚠ Do not let anyone stand up on this trolley.

3. Let the childen bring their bikes, skateboards, roller skates, soap box trolleys. Try these out to show how movement is easier with wheels.

To discuss

Which of all the methods is the best way of moving a load. The idea of reducing friction should begin to emerge. At the very least children should get a *feel* for it.

More or less friction

When one object slides over another, the smoother their surfaces the less friction there is between them. Sometimes we want more friction to stop things from moving sometimes we want less.

For children to do

Find a block of wood about 15 x 7 x 3 cm. Sandpaper one of the largest surfaces until it is smooth. Fix a screw eye to one end.

1. Pull the block along a table. Is more pull needed to start it moving than to keep it moving? Find the pull needed to move the block on different surfaces. Measure the stretch of a thin rubber band, or use a spring scale. Make sure the test is fair. Always measure either the pull needed to start the block moving, *or* the pull needed to keep it moving once it has started.

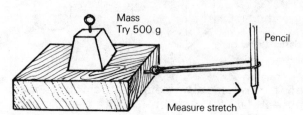

Mass
Try 500 g

Pencil

Measure stretch

Smooth surface underneath

2. Does water on a vinyl tiled floor make the block easier to move, or more difficult.

Vinyl tiles	Pull
Dry	
Wet	
Oil	

Surface	Pull
Polished wood floor	
Asphalt playground	
Vinyl tiles	
Carpet	

Try using other things on this kind of floor: oil, detergent solution, French chalk or talc. Remind the children to clean the floor thoroughly afterwards so people do not slip.

⚠

To discuss

Relate the children's findings to their everyday experiences. We need friction between our shoes and the floor to stop us from falling down, the smoother our shoe soles and the smoother the floor, the less friction. Water and oil reduce friction, we are more likely to fall on a wet or a greasy floor, and cars are more likely to skid on wet or greasy roads as the tyres cannot grip well. Water in brake drums causes brakes to fail. But if we want to *reduce* friction we often use oil or wax, for example we oil hinges and moving parts of machinery, we wax drawer runners.

Easier lifting – ramps

You will need a number of lengths of wood, at least 3, say 0.5 metre, 1 metre and 1.5 metres.

For children to do
Pile a load onto a fairly large toy lorry, about 20 cm long, or a small wheeled truck. Find which is the easiest ramp to pull the lorry up to get it onto a small chair. Make a record.

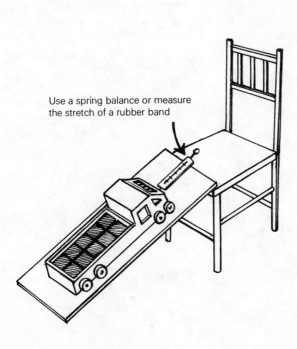

Use a spring balance or measure the stretch of a rubber band

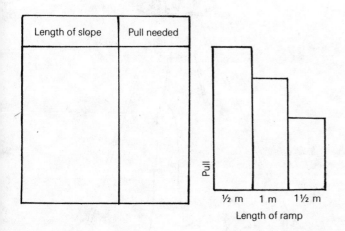

Length of slope	Pull needed

Pull / Length of ramp: ½ m · 1 m · 1½ m

To discuss
The effect of lengthening the ramp is to reduce the effort needed to lift the load. What if it was lifted without a ramp? Would that be more difficult? Try putting a sling round the lorry and finding the pull needed to lift it. Talk about the practical application of this and the use made of it: wheelbarrows on ramps, zig-zag roads up mountains, sloping paths to footbridges, luggage trolley slopes in airports, slipways for boats.

Easier lifting – levers

We constantly use levers, both to move our own bodies and to do simple, everyday jobs.

For children to do
1. How many to lift the teacher?

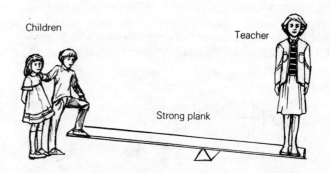

Children   Teacher   Strong plank

Change the place of the pivot. Make a record. Sketch the results or use gummed paper shapes to make pictures.

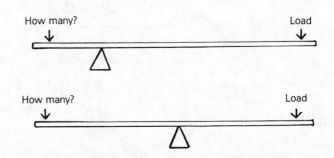

How many?   Load

2. Open an unsprung door. Where is the easiest place to push it shut?

To discuss
Common uses of levers – let children try them if possible. Levering up a spadeful of earth; extracting nails with a claw-hammer; using a table knife; lifting with a crow-bar; levering open a paint or syrup tin. We use many double levers. Get children to collect examples and try them out: secateurs; scissors; wire cutters; nut-crackers; tongs for sugar, cooking, coal; shears.

Falling over

We are constantly, although subconsciously, keeping our balance. Our muscles work hard to overcome gravity.

For children to do
Let the children build some four-legged creatures. You will need boxes (shoe boxes will be excellent), toilet roll tubes and kitchen roll tubes. You can add heads and tails if you wish. Invent some names. Where do you have to put the legs for greatest stability? Which is the more difficult to knock over, the short-legged or the long-legged beast?

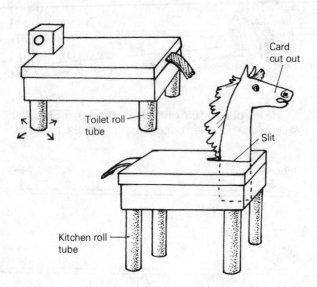

Toilet roll tube

Card cut out

Slit

Kitchen roll tube

Now make a two-legged creature. Turn the box on end. How steady are these? Where is it best to put the legs for greatest stability?

To discuss
Compare two-legged creatures with four-legged ones. Which are more likely to fall over? What if the creature had legs of paper, would these hold it up?

Keeping a balance

For children to do
Make the *daredevil* tight rope walker. Balance him on one leg on your finger. What else can you balance him on? Give him a Plasticine hat. Does he still balance? If not, try adding more Plasticine to his hands.

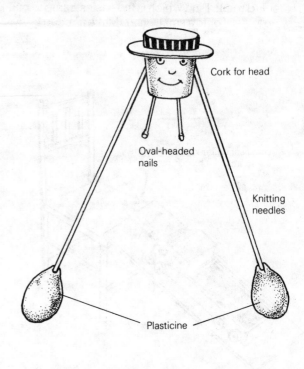

Cork for head

Oval-headed nails

Knitting needles

Plasticine

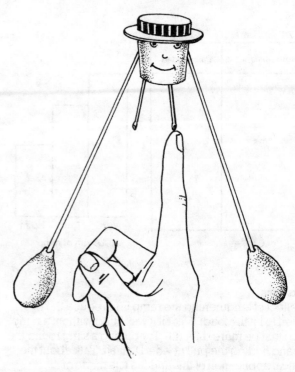

To discuss
Toppling over, buses, containers. How a low centre of gravity gives stability and balance.

Throw a paper plane

Many things can change the flight of a paper plane. The design, the way it is thrown, and the nose weight can affect the flight.

For children to do
Make a standard model. Use A4 paper.

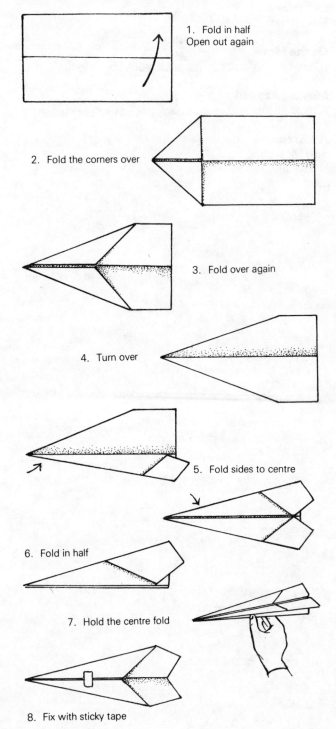

1. Fold in half
Open out again

2. Fold the corners over

3. Fold over again

4. Turn over

5. Fold sides to centre

6. Fold in half

7. Hold the centre fold

8. Fix with sticky tape

To discuss
How far the dart goes. Which is the best way to get it to fly straight? Try adding a paper-clip or two as nose weights. Discuss if this makes flight better.

Dropping a paper helicopter

For children to do
Here is how to make a paper helicopter. A piece of paper 20 cm long and 6 cm wide is needed. Measure, mark and cut the paper like this. Ask children to drop their helicopters. Time how long each takes to spin to the floor. What can be done that might change this? Try adding a *load* (more paper-clips). Perhaps the wing size will make a difference?

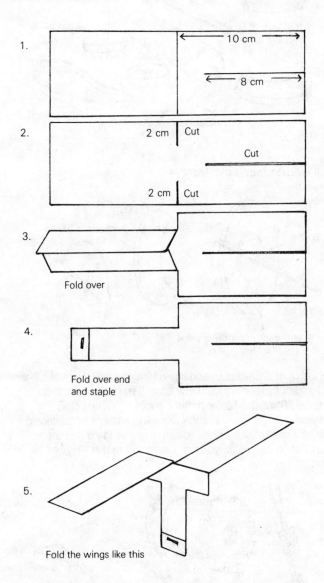

1.

10 cm

8 cm

2.

2 cm | Cut

Cut

2 cm | Cut

3.

Fold over

4.

Fold over end and staple

5.

Fold the wings like this

Try making 4 cm or 6 cm cuts instead of 8 cm. Try making the helicopter with a different kind of paper. What might happen if the wing gets damaged? Try using a punch to make holes in the wing. Cut off part of a wing. What do you think will happen if you let go of it differently? Try holding the wings together and letting go.

To discuss
The effect of changing the load, changing the wing size, changing the way of dropping the helicopter. The fact that the helicopter can fly only if a person lifts it up (transfers energy to it).

Winding up a cotton reel tractor

For children to do
Here is how to make a cotton reel tractor. You will need these things.

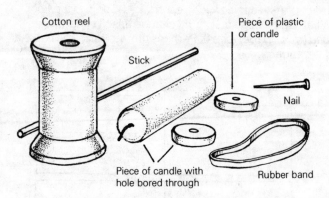

Cotton reel

Stick

Piece of plastic or candle

Nail

Piece of candle with hole bored through

Rubber band

Put them together like this:

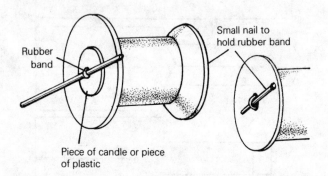

Rubber band

Small nail to hold rubber band

Piece of candle or piece of plastic

Wind up the tractor by the stick. How far will it travel? Wind up and count the winds. How far will it go with 10 winds, 20 winds, 40 winds? Make it climb a slope. What is the steepest slope it will climb? Does the surface of the slope make a difference? Try a rough surface. Try a smooth surface. What might you try that would make a better tractor?

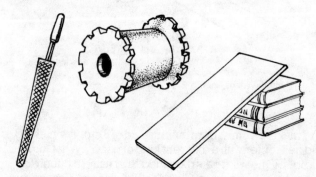

Perhaps a different stick: longer, heavier? Perhaps a different rubber band: thicker, longer? Perhaps notching the edge of the cotton reel?

To discuss
The factors that affect the speed of the tractor and that affect the distance it will travel. The idea that energy needed by the tank came from the person who wound the band.

More to do

The Learning Through Science packs named below contain the following cards that could be adapted for use with slow learning children.

Ourselves
How Do You Rate
Leg Power
Dem Bones, Dem Bones

On the Move
Almost all the cards in this pack would be relevant.

Moving Around
Almost all the cards in this pack would be relevant.

All Around
Bird Movements
Study One
Snail Ways

GET THE MESSAGE

This section introduces children with learning difficulties to several methods of communication. It suggests some scientific ways of examining the effectiveness of the methods, and helps the children to explore some of the scientific principles involved, such as the ways in which sound travels.

Contents

Send a message

Collect pictures or objects which illustrate different ways of sending messages. Use them to introduce the topic. How many ways can children think of? Who uses, or used, them? When and where?

For children to do

1. Whisper a message along a line. Try these. How much do they change? *(i)* Saturday. *(ii)* The school is on fire. *(iii)* Miss says we are going to the zoo on Monday. Does a message change more if it is longer.

2. *Speak* a message along a line. Go out of the room to pass it on.

3. Try sending a message without using a voice. *Mouth* a short message. Can anybody interpret it?

4. Mime messages for other children to guess (actors pretend they cannot speak). Ask the way to a station. Order a drink. Explain to a chemist that you have a sore throat

To discuss

The ways of sending messages, and what we need to pass on a message to people near to us.

Body messages

The way man uses facial expressions, gestures and postures to communicate is an important area to study.

For children to do

1. *(i)* Make happy/sad faces using paper plates. Cut a paper plate in half. Use one half to cover half of another whole plate, and stick it in place with sticky tape. Flip the half plate up and draw a happy expression. Flip it down and draw a sad expression. What is the main thing that is different?

(ii) Ask friends to look anxious, sad, happy, cross, bored. Notice how eyebrows help to convey feelings. Draw the *changes* in the faces.

(iii) Discuss with the children how these simple changes of facial gestures are one of man's most potent forms of communication.

2. Mime receiving a parcel and finding something nice inside. Mime receiving a parcel and finding something broken inside. Mime being frightened by a loud noise.

To discuss and demonstrate

The versatility of gestures: the finger that beckons, the begging hand, the threatening fist, the wave of greeting. Use your hands to say: No, Stop, Quiet, Go, Come. Discuss with children how they would express fear, anger, pity, kindliness without using speech.

74

Talking and listening 1

For children to do

1. Feel the *voice*. Children should gently rest their fingers against their *Adam's apple*, and talk to a friend. Discuss what they feel? Try whispering, shouting, singing, laughing. What do they feel?

2. Speak into the open end of the tin. Gently feel the stretched balloon with fingertips. Make loud and soft sounds. What differences do the children feel?

Tin with both ends removed

Piece of balloon fixed by rubber band

3. Make a speaking tube. The top halves of squeezy bottles can be used as funnels.

Plastic funnel

5 m of hose pipe

Must it be straight?

Cut

To discuss
The fact that voices make vibrations and the louder the noise the bigger the vibrations. We usually hear through air, but when the vibrations are shut in a tube they travel even better.

Talking and listening 2

For children to do
Make large paper cones to use as megaphones and ear trumpets. Test them outside.

Test 1 Does the megaphone help a message? Shout without the megaphone. Children stand with their backs to the shouter. Shout with the megaphone.

Test 2 Does the ear trumpet help?

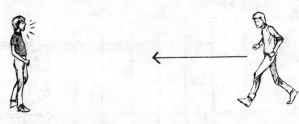

Walk towards a child shouting a message. Stop when the message is clearly heard. First test without an ear trumpet, then with one.

Test 3 Use a megaphone and an ear trumpet. Can the message be heard over a greater distance?

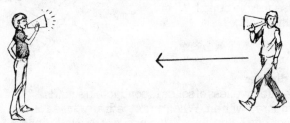

To discuss
Using a megaphone to direct the sound helps a voice to travel further. Trumpets also help to collect the vibrations. Look at ears on deer, rabbits, cats, dogs, horses. Does the size of the megaphone and ear trumpet affect their efficiency.

Using your ears

Generally sound travels further and better through solid things than through air, and the more dense the solid the better. Wood and metal are good sound conductors.

For the children to do

1. Move *towards* the watch. Stop after each pace and listen through the air. Listen through the table. Stop when they hear the watch.

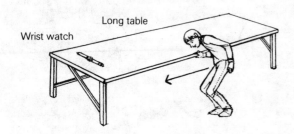

Test each other.

Measure and record the distances.

Name	Distance through table	Distance in air

2. How far can they hear through air. How far through railings? Make a record.

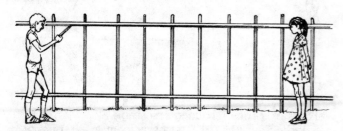

3. Each child holds a clean pencil in his mouth *without* closing his teeth on it, then taps the pencil with another one. Repeat with teeth *closed* on the pencil. What do they notice?

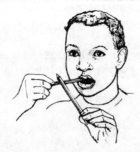

To discuss

The effectiveness of solids in conducting sounds, compared with air. When one's teeth are closed on the pencil one hears through the bones of the skull, hence through solid, so the sounds are much louder than through air. Partially deaf people can often hear well on the telephone. Talk about Red Indians listening with their ears to the ground; try this in a field or playground. Also see *Me and My Friends*, page 9 and Learning Through Science, *Ourselves*, the card *Hear Hear*, Macdonald, 1981.

Telephone messages

All children should know how to use a telephone, both in everyday life and in an emergency.

For the children to do

1. Learn how to use a telephone, both private and public. Learn how to dial 999 and to spell a name. Make up a little play with the caller, the operator and the emergency service. If possible let the children use the telephone. Dial the numbers for the time, the weather, travel information etc.

2. Make a *telephone*. *Discover* that the string has to be taut before anything can be heard.

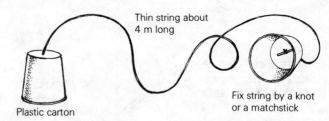

Thin string about 4 m long

Fix string by a knot or a matchstick

Plastic carton

What could be done to make a better telephone. Change only one thing at a time.

i) Try different string: thicker, nylon, or perhaps thin wire.

ii) Try different ear pieces.

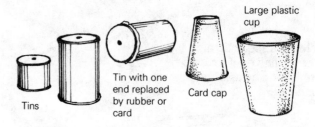

Large plastic cup

Tin with one end replaced by rubber or card

Card cap

Tins

iii) Perhaps the string could be wetted or waxed?

iv) Perhaps a button or paper-clip would be better at the end of the string?

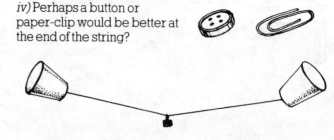

Try a weight hung in the middle to keep it taut.

3. How far can you send a message with your best telephone?

To discuss

The *fairness* of the tests. Was only one thing at a time changed? Could the *listener* hear the message *without* the telephone? In this case vibrations pass along the string or wire.

Other messages in sound

Bells, whistles and sirens bring us many messages. Can children recognise them?

For the children to do
1. Find different examples of bell, whistle and siren messages. Tape record as many as possible. Now test each other. Make a record.

Name	Telephone	Doorbell	Alarm clock	School bell	Kettle whistle	Police car
John	✓	✗	✗	✓	✓	✓
Sue	✓	✓	✓	✓	✗	✗

2. Find how well sounds carry. Children stand well apart, facing away from the sound. Put up a hand when the sound is heard. Make a record.

	John	Peter	Susan	Alison	James	Robert
Recorder	✓	✓	✓	✓	✓	✓
Triangle	✓	✓	✗	✗	✗	✗

3. Do low sounds travel better than high sounds? Use a recorder and test in the same way.

To discuss
That high sounds travel further than low sounds, and loud sounds further than soft ones. Alarm and message sounds are usually high and loud, and startling.

Papers and pencils

The use of evidence to justify statements is an important part of science. These activities will help children to learn to do this and to sort out the values of attributes for different purposes.

For children to do
Collect as many papers as possible.
1. Grade them by *thickness*.

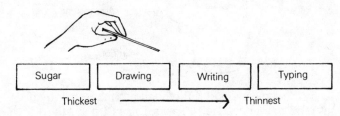

Sugar	Drawing	Writing	Typing

Thickest ──────────→ Thinnest

2. Grade them by *smoothness*.

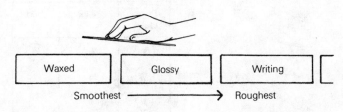

Waxed	Glossy	Writing

Smoothest ──────────→ Roughest

3. Grade them by *transparency/opaqueness*. Use a piece of bold print and lay the paper on top. Can the print be seen? If so try two sheets.

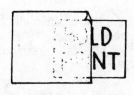

Writing	Typing	Greaseproof	Tracing

Most opaque ──────────→ Least opaque

4. Try to put the papers in the best order for writing a message with an HB pencil. Try writing a name and address on each. Does this make the children want to change the order of the papers? Why?

5. On the best paper try different pencils. Try to rub out the marks with an eraser. Which pencil is liked the best?

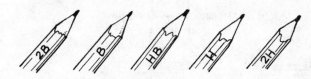

To discuss
The justifications for choices made and the attributes needed by writing paper and pencils.

Inks and felt tips

For children to do

1. Make an ink blot on blotting paper with Parker Quink permanent black ink. Carefully add water drop by drop to the *middle* of an ink blot. Let each drop soak in before the next is added.

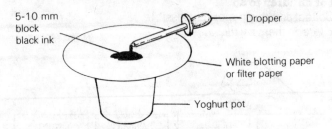

5-10 mm block black ink

Dropper

White blotting paper or filter paper

Yoghurt pot

2. Try the same method with other liquid inks (not Indian ink) and water based felt tip pens. Dry and mount the *chromatograms*.

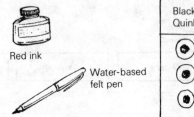

Red ink

Water-based felt pen

Black Quink	Black felt-tip	Red ink
◉	◉	◉
◉	◉	
◉	◉	

3. Find out whether all *black* water based felt pens have the same pigments. Collect together as many makes as possible. Make and mount chromatograms.

4. Find what made the mixture. After finding the component pigments of coloured inks ask children to make blots of two mixed together. Ask other children to drop water onto the blots to try to find which colours were mixed.

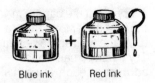

Blue ink + Red ink

5. Try out some old recipes for inks. Test to find which is best.

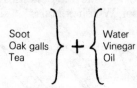

Soot
Oak galls
Tea

+

Water
Vinegar
Oil

To discuss
The colours which are produced by mixing different pigments. Can we make the same colours by mixing paints? Try this. Talk about what pigments are and where they come from.

Sending a letter

Colour *speaks*. Postage stamps are colour coded in order to make differentiation between values clear. The following activity will involve children in a sorting and separating exercise which explores how colour helps in communication.

For children to do

1. Collect used examples of the current definitive Great Britain postage stamps. Mount them in a display to show the range of colours. How many colours are there?

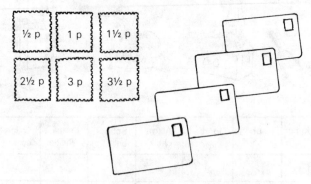

½ p   1 p   1½ p

2½ p   3 p   3½ p

2. Make up a range of post-cards: three with blue stamps (you could colour a square blue on each card), three with red stamps, three with brown stamps, three with green stamps. Mix them up randomly. Find how long it takes people to sort them into the four stamp colours.

Name	Time

3. Now find how long it takes them to sort cards, using shapes and then using letters.

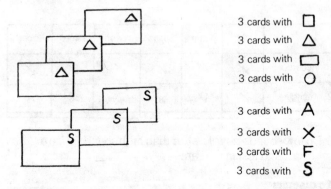

3 cards with ☐
3 cards with △
3 cards with ▭
3 cards with ○

3 cards with A
3 cards with X
3 cards with F
3 cards with S

To discuss
Which helps sorting postcards best, colour, shapes or letters?

Messages in flags

Many messages are sent by flags. Their effectiveness depends on how easily the colours and pattern of the flags are seen.

For the children to do

1. Find which colours are seen in poor light. Use coloured spots stuck to card and placed in the bottom of the tin. Use different backgrounds: colours on white, colours on black. Start with all the holes plugged.

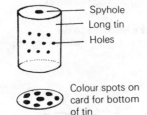

Spyhole
Long tin
Holes

Colour spots on card for bottom of tin

Uncover them one at a time until a colour can be identified. Note how many holes had to be uncovered before the first colour could be identified on each background. Make a record.

Background colour	Colour seen first	Holes unplugged
White	Red	4

2. Find the difference the background makes if the colours are far away. Use A4 size sheets of sugar paper and coloured gummed strips to make some *flags*. Test outside. Start a good distance away. Move nearer. Each child should make his own record. Repeat with different backgrounds.

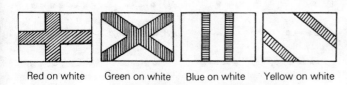

Red on white   Green on white   Blue on white   Yellow on white

Distance paces	1	2	3	4
100				
75				
50				

To discuss

The best colours for poor light; the best contrasts of colour. The use of flags for sending messages, white flags, Blue Peter, red flags for traffic, firing ranges, dangerous bathing, green flags for trains and traffic, ship's messages in flags.

Finding by feeling

For children to do

1. Make some *feely* or *blind* bags or boxes. By *touch* only, children try to identify a collection of objects inside a box; sort a collection of shapes; sort a collection of fabrics; sort a collection of coins.

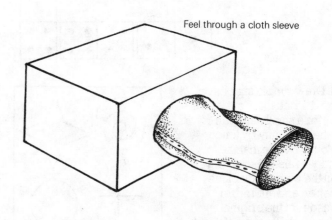

Feel through a cloth sleeve

2. Make a collection of screws of different lengths and diameters. Blindfolded children try to sort them out.

3. Make a touch maze. Use small patches of different textures to direct a blindfolded child through the maze. How many children can find their way?

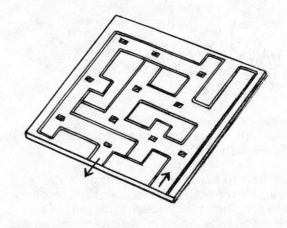

To discuss

The great sensitivity of our fingers. Are other parts of our bodies equally good at sorting by touch: toes and cheeks? To identify a shape most people need to *handle* an object.

See Learning Through Science, *Ourselves* the card *With Feeling*, Macdonald, 1981.

Feeling a message

For children to do

1. Pairs of blindfolded children play a game with *relief* dominoes. A third *sighted* child may need to help.

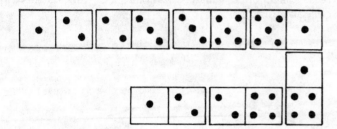

2. Draw simple shapes on card. Prick them out with a pin or a small nail. Can others identify by touch alone? *Notice* that the ridges raised by the pin are on the wrong side of the paper, and are mirror images of the original drawings. Beware of this if children prick out letters.*

3. How well can we feel the ground through our shoes? Let pairs of children lead a blindfolded friend across different surfaces. What can the blindfolded child tell about the surfaces? Can he identify any of them? How does he know? Try outside on grass, paved path, gravel path, asphalt playground. Try inside.

To discuss

Show the children some Braille print, and discuss with them the difficulties of being blind.

Scientists have recently been trying to find out whether special surfaces on footpaths would help blind people to avoid obstacles and to find pedestrian crossings. Grooves, raised blobs and raised wavy ridges have been tried and are all easily identified through shoes, even by blindfolded sighted people.

For more information about the blind write to The Royal National Institute for the Blind, 224 Great Portland Street, LONDON W1.

*See *Me and my reflection*, page 19.

Messages in code

Samuel Morse invented the Morse Code so that messages could be sent over a distance by flashes of light or buzzes of sound. These activities encourage really careful observation and analysis, and give great stimulus to reading and spelling.

For children to do

1. Make a flasher* or use a torch which has a flasher.

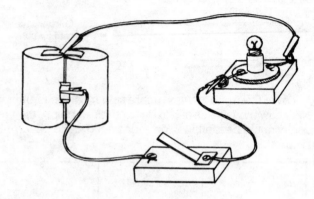

Use the Morse code to send messages to each other.

A ●—	J ●———	S ●●●	2 ●●———
B —●●●	K —●—	T —	3 ●●●——
C —●—●	L ●—●●	U ●●—	4 ●●●●—
D —●●	M ——	V ●●●—	5 ●●●●●
E ●	N —●	W ●——	6 —●●●●
F ●●—●	O ———	X —●●—	7 ——●●●
G ——●	P ●——●	Y —●——	8 ———●●
H ●●●●	Q ——●—	Z ——●●	9 ————●
I ●●	R ●—●	1 ●————	10 —————

2. Make up their own code for written messages. Use substitute letters or numbers or symbols.

Letters	Numbers	Symbols
For A B C D	For A B C D	For A B C D E
Write E F G H	Write 1 2 3 4	Write △□⊬⊥○

To discuss

Important Morse message – S O S.
How might you go about breaking the second type of code? Think about the most frequent letters at the ends of words and in words.

*See *Batteries and bulbs*, page 91.

Invisible messages

These depend on chemical changes which turn an invisible substance into a visible one.

For children to do
1. Make invisible ink. Dissolve one teaspoonful of copper sulphate in water. Stir well.

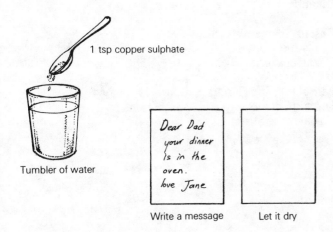

1 tsp copper sulphate

Tumbler of water

Write a message · Let it dry

Dear Dad your dinner is in the oven. love Jane

 Copper sulphate is poisonous so must be handled carefully

The receiver of the message must dab the paper with cotton wool soaked in a developing liquid. Dissolve 2 teaspoonsful of washing soda in water.

2 tsp washing soda

Tumbler of water

2. Write messages with common liquids which disappear when they dry and are developed by heat by placing on a hot radiator.

Try: milk, sugar water, lemon juice, orange juice, onion juice, vinegar, Coca Cola.

To discuss
The agents of change, which may be other substances, or may be physical conditions such as heat. Other examples of changes brought about in these ways are sugar and salt dissolved in water*; butter, ice, eggs, cake mixtures, potatoes changed by heat.

*See *Making a Cup of Tea*, page 107.

Signs and symbols around us

It would be a good idea to walk the route you would use for the first activity in advance and on your own, so that you have a chance to notice the signs and symbols.

For children to do
1. Go for a short walk near the school. Look for signs and symbols: road signs, shop and pub signs, trade marks, shields or crests. Make a list. Compare lists, including the teacher's list. Were any signs missed? If so, can the children think why, e.g. height, colour.

| Sign | Colour | Where | | | What it means |
		High ↗	Eye level →	Low ↙	*Fill in this column afterwards in school*
In School Lane (30)	Red on white	✓			
In Laburnum Grove	Black on white		✓		

2. How well do the signs do their job? Draw and colour a range of local signs on A5 card. Each child might do one. Put all together and use as flash cards to test each other. They could be extended to include signs the children *ought* to know.

To discuss
The importance of recognising some of these signs, and how quickly signs and symbols can convey their meaning. What makes the signs noticeable: shape, size, colour, pattern?

Children could design their own signs for features in the school.

Animal messages

These activities will encourage children to look particularly carefully at other creatures in their environment. Animals communicate in many ways by body language, by scent, by sound, by pattern of colour, by movement. Children might first look at cats, dogs and other pets.

For children to do

1. Discuss how people communicate with their pets. List the words that dogs and cats seem to *understand*. List or draw the actions they *understand*.

2. How do animals communicate with people and with each other? Dogs with each other, cats with dogs, horses with people and so on. Find pictures of dogs and cats. How do the animals feel? Ask children to give reasons for their answers.

3. Wild dogs live in packs, but cats are solitary animals. Observe and discuss the behaviour of pet dogs and cats. Does it reflect the pack or solitary lives of their ancestors and wild relations?

4. In the spring, watch and discuss the way birds display and defend their nesting territory, and warn each other of enemies such as cats.

To discuss

Why animals need to communicate. The training of animals, especially police dogs, guide dogs. If possible invite a trained dog and its owner to school.

More to do

The Learning Through Science packs named below contain the following cards (in addition to those mentioned in this section) that could be adapted for use with slow learning children.

Ourselves
Listen!

Colour
Paints and Painters
Colour at Work
Looking at Colour
Being Seen and Hiding
Finding Colour
Colour in the Street

BALLS AND BALL GAMES

This section helps children with learning difficulties to use all the steps of scientific enquiry to find out about some of the attributes of a variety of balls. Consideration of these attributes and of the structure and material of the balls will help children to appreciate that the form and properties of materials influence their use.

Contents

A collection of balls

Encourage children to bring balls from home to add to a collection of school balls.

For children to do
1. Make and display a collection of balls used for all sorts of purposes, not *only* for games.

2. Handle and talk about the balls. Put them into sets according to different criteria: such as balls used for team games/individual games; kicked/thrown/hit/moved another way; balls for some other purpose.

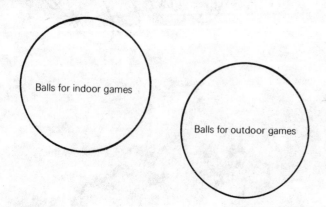

To discuss
The uses of the balls. More about ball games: the other equipment used, where the games are played, famous players.

Balls appear in different sets according to the criteria used; an *understanding* important for scientific classification.

Which ball is the best roller?

Looking for relationships is an important part of science, and children should be encouraged to think about whether simple relationships exist or not. For this work a long level run will be needed, such as a corridor.

For children to do
Talk about balls used for rolling games.
Ask the children to choose three balls which they think will roll well.

Large plastic ball

Marble

Write down which one they think will roll furthest.
Now test to find out.
The balls must *not* be pushed.

Solid heavy ball: billiard ball shinty ball cricket ball

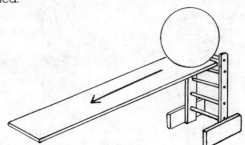

Try out the equipment. Do any of the balls roll in a curve? Can the children devise a way to stop this?

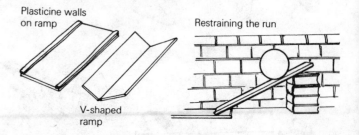

Plasticine walls on ramp

V-shaped ramp

Restraining the run

Ask the children to do the test, mark the floor where each ball stops and, if you wish, measure the distance. Roll each ball twice. Compare the rolls, find the order of rolling.

To discuss
The best roller. Did anybody predict correctly? Was it the biggest ball (see page 88)? Was it the heaviest ball (see page 89)?

The need for more than one rolling. Did any ball stop in the same place twice? What if we roll three times? Some children may wish to improve the fairness of the test by comparing large and small balls of the same materials, for example plastic; or by comparing light and heavy balls of the same size.

Follow up work
How will the results change if the ramp is raised or lowered?

Which ball bounces best?

This will help the children to understand about fair tests. You will need to devise a reasonably accurate method of observing and marking the bounce.

For children to do
Ask the children to choose five balls which they think will bounce well. Discuss what is meant by a good bouncer. Now ask them which of the five they think will bounce best. Test to find out.

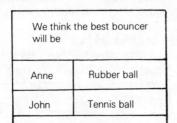

We think the best bouncer will be	
Anne	Rubber ball
John	Tennis ball

Marker must watch the wall not the ball and mark height of bounce

Drop the ball

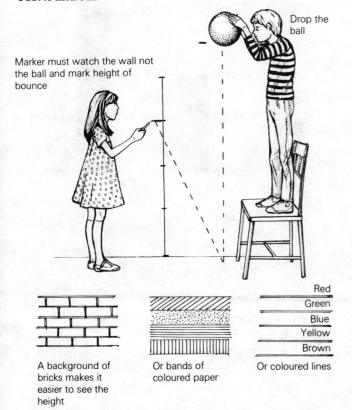

A background of bricks makes it easier to see the height

Or bands of coloured paper

Red
Green
Blue
Yellow
Brown

Or coloured lines

Test each ball twice.

The marks on the wall can be a good record of this test. Alternatively a strip of paper can be cut or the heights measured.

To discuss
The best bouncer. Did anyone predict correctly? Let it be clearly understood that there is no question of being *wrong*. Predicting, then testing to see if our ideas are correct is the way scientists work. The fairness of each test bounce. Did the dropper always drop from the mark? Was the bounce always measured accurately?

What do the children think is important for bounce, size, or mass, or material? See pages 88-89.

Choose some balls they think will be *poor* bouncers and test them.

Does the surface help the bounce?

This introduces another variable. It also shows that the properties of the surface affect the bounce; some are elastic, and tend to help poor bouncers and hinder good ones; some become deformed by all the balls and help none to bounce.

For children to do
Ask the children to choose two balls.

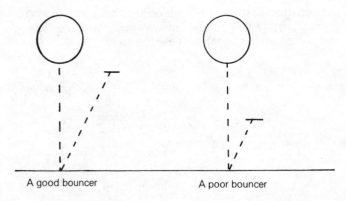

A good bouncer

A poor bouncer

Drop the balls on three different surfaces: on a hard surface, such as concrete; on grass; on a P.E. mat or thick carpet.

Ask the children to predict which will be the best bouncing surface for each ball.
Test each ball twice.

To discuss
Which was the best bouncing surface? Was it the same for both the balls?
Did anything take the bounce out of the best bouncer?
Did anything help the poor bouncer to do better?
Did it ever bounce higher than the best bouncer?

Further work
Test some games balls on the different surfaces. Does a ball bounce best on the surface it is intended for?

Dropping Plasticine balls

This is an interesting extension of page 85 and poses a problem for children which previous work may help them to solve.

For children to do
Make three Plasticine balls, each about the size of a tennis ball. Ask whether the children think these balls will bounce?

1. Drop them from three heights on to a hard floor. Record by making into prints of the flattened surfaces. Take care not to press so hard as to increase the area.

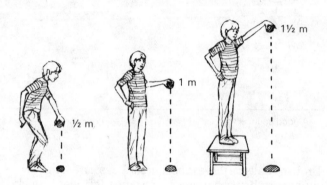

2. Ask the children if they can find a way of making a Plasticine ball bounce. Remind them of what happened when the poor bouncer dropped on to a P.E. mat or carpet. *a) Drop* ball onto a thick piece of foam or a thick foam cushion. *b) Throw* the ball down onto the same surface.

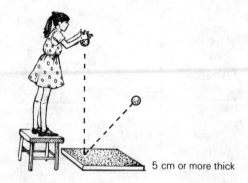

5 cm or more thick

To discuss
1. The flattening of the balls when they drop on a hard surface. Is there a pattern?

2. That *bounce* may be entirely in the surface a ball is falling onto. Poking foam and then watching it reform will help children to understand about its bounce.

3. Take a ball which bounces well. Push it hard and steadily against the floor or a wall, and watch it flatten. Now slowly release it, and watch it *quickly* regain its shape. This is what happens when a ball drops and bounces. It is pushed upwards as it regains its shape.

Will a bigger drop make a higher bounce?

If children are still interested in bouncing balls, ask this question. Two scientific ideas are involved: that raising an object to a higher level increases the energy it can release when it falls, and that there may be patterns in experimental results.

For children to do
If we drop the ball from twice the height, will it bounce twice as high? Test to find out. Drop the ball twice from each height. Either make a chart or mark the wall.

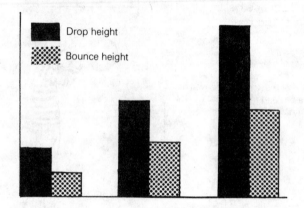

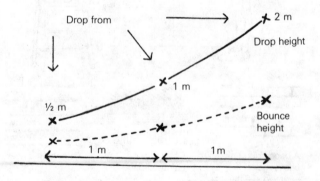

Now try a second ball.
If you are marking the wall, drop from the same positions as before and make another bounce height line.

To discuss
When the balls fell from two metres did they bounce higher than when they fell from half a metre?

Did the ball that bounced higher from two metres also bounce higher from one metre, and from half a metre? Look for patterns in the results.

Try to extend the children's thinking to the idea that as the ball falls further, the bounce gets higher, and that there is a pattern to the increase. This is not a direct relationship, so twice the drop height does *not* give twice the bounce height. It will be satisfying if any children are able to see that the drop heights and the bounce heights have a similar pattern.

Bouncing off

This looks at the relationship between the angle at which a ball strikes a surface and the angle at which it returns.

Preparation
Prepare beforehand with or without the children's help.

Find a smooth level surface which has a wall at right angles. Draw a semicircle and mark in five radii.

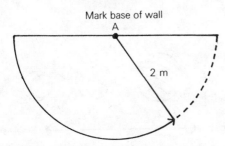

Mark base of wall
A

2 m

Use 2 m of string to mark a semi-circle

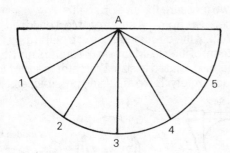

A

1
2
3
4
5

Mark these lines and numbers

For children to do
1. Choose a ball which rolls and bounces well.

2. Ask where the children think the ball will return to if they roll it from point 3 to hit the wall at A.

3. Test to find out. Roll the ball twice.

4. Will the same thing happen if the ball is rolled from point 2, and point 1? Predict and test. Mark where each returning ball crosses the half circle.

5. Does it work the other way round? Roll from points 4 and 5.

To discuss
Can any *rule* be seen regarding the roll line and the return line?
Can the children now mark a rolling line of their own and predict in chalk the return line?
Do all balls behave in this way, or only good bouncers?

Further work
It would be interesting to see a bowl curve as it rolled. Discuss why and how the direction of the curve could be controlled.

What makes a ball difficult to catch?

This is most likely to be successful if the children have designed their own fair test. It demonstrates the dangers of drawing conclusions without considering how a test was done.

For children to do
Choose three very different balls.

An airflow ball

A cricket ball

A netball

How easy are they to catch? Ask each child to try to catch each ball three times. How will the test be done? Who will throw the balls? Overhand or underhand? Over what distance?

Perhaps one person should throw all the balls, the teacher or an older child? Perhaps children should work in pairs, and throw to each other in turn?

Ball	Catches			How many catches?
	1	2	3	

To discuss
Problems of the fair test. Did throwers grow careless?
The children's ideas of what made balls easy or difficult to catch, and any supporting evidence. The size of the ball, its mass, its structure, the material it was made of might all make a difference.
Discuss games which involve catching balls.

Further work
How do we get on using only right hands or left hands?
Does this link with right- or left-handedness?
Try catching other things such as bean bags or Frisbies.
How do results compare with balls?

What are the balls made of?

It would be interesting to draw the children's attention to the material from which the balls are made. As this section focuses attention on what children do with balls, it will give some understanding of the nature and properties of the materials involved.

For children to do
Ask them to choose five balls from the collection. Discuss the headings of the table below, then ask them to complete it for the balls they have chosen. An alternative would be to tape record their observations.

	Hard or soft?	What is the outside made of?	Solid or hollow?
○			
⊙			
⊛			
◐			
○			

To discuss
The children's observations. What are the commonest materials for balls to be made of? Where do they come from? What else are they used for?

Solid and hollow balls. Cut through an old tennis ball, unravel an old golf ball, blow up a football or a plastic ball.

Think back to other practical activities in this section: rolling balls, bouncing balls, catching balls. What was the *best* ball in each group made of? How can it be described in terms of size, heaviness, solidity and material? For example, large, light, hollow, plastic, small, heavy, solid, metal.

See Learning Through Science, *Materials*, Macdonald, 1982.

Balls in order of size

This poses the problem of how to measure a sphere. The results link with earlier activities in this section. Start with the balls used for rolling (page 84) or catching (page 87). Add to them if you wish. Or use another range of five balls, including some of very similar size.

For children to do
Assemble the balls you have decided to use.
Get the children to predict the order of size. Record this prediction.

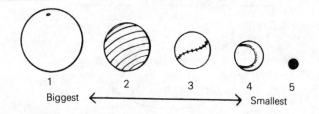

1 Biggest ⟵⟶ 5 Smallest

Is it right?
How can we be sure?
How can we measure the size of a ball?
Encourage ideas from the children. Most children appreciate that the circumference of a ball is a measurement of its size. Many do not understand that the diameter is also related to size. Diameter is easier to measure accurately. Here are some possibilities.

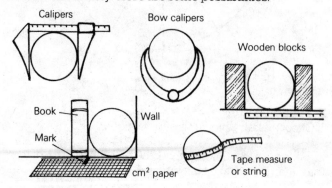

Make a chart.

To discuss
The predicted and measured order of size. Was anybody right? Would another method of measuring give the same order? Look for relationships between the sizes of the balls and the rolling and catching tests.
Did size seem to have anything to do with rolling or catching?

Further work
1. Use compasses to draw discs the size of the balls. Display them. Discuss the difference between discs and spheres.

2. Draw the size of holes some balls have to go into or through: basketball net, netball ring; golf hole, croquet hoop, cricket stumps (*not* to pass through).
Compare the sizes of ball and hole, and think about the way each game is played. From how far away do players have to try to get the ball into the hole?

Balls in order of heaviness

This gives the children practice in weighing and in the language of comparative heaviness. It will help them to understand that large things are not always the heaviest.

For children to do
Assemble the five balls used for rolling (page 84) or some other activity in this section. Make sure that a large, light ball, and a small, heavy ball are included.
Ask the children to put the balls in order of mass. They should hold two balls, one in each hand, and try to decide which is heavier, then replace one with another, and so on. Each child should make a record of the order she predicts. See the table below.
Ask how she can find whose prediction was right.
Check the order by using a beam balance.
If the children are not going to weigh the balls, omit the *mass* column from the tables.
Alternatively weigh the balls.

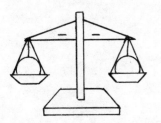 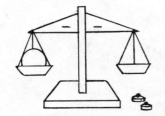

Ball	Guess order	Mass	Real order

To discuss
Compare the children's results with their predictions.
Does the size of a thing tell us about its heaviness?
Was the biggest ball the heaviest? Was the smallest the lightest?
What things do you know which are: small and heavy (fishing line sinker); large and light (balloon, big piece of polystyrene)?

Thinking back to the rolling balls (page 84) was the best roller the lightest or the heaviest ball? Did heaviness seem to make any difference to rolling?

Further work
1. Weigh a clean, dry, leather football.
Weigh it again after a wet, muddy match.
Which is the heaviest ball you can find? Which is the lightest you can find? Try some of the practical activities with these.
Which one can you throw the furthest?

A final discussion

You might like to round off this piece of work by talking with the children about the purposes for which each ball was designed, in terms of various attributes they have examined: size, heaviness, material, bounciness and so on. What are the features of each ball that make it particularly suitable for its purpose?

Suggestions for further work
1. Which types of ball are most easily kicked: *a)* a given distance, *b)* to reach a particular point?

2. How easy is it to pat bounce the balls?

3. Which types of ball are easy to hit accurately with different types of bat, racquet, baton and stick.

4. How far does a ball travel through the air? Make a simple catapult.

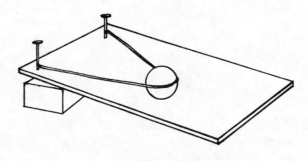

a) Use a fixed slope and roll down it different balls.
b) Use the same ball and roll it down different slopes.

5. What happens when balls collide? Use marbles on a curved curtain track:

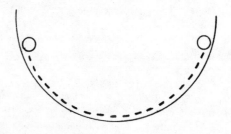

a) two similar marbles,
b) one large and one small marble,
c) two small marbles on one side, one on the other and so on.

Other references
If you wish to extend this work there are many more suggestions and some background information in two of the Science 5/13 books.
Science from Toys, p.52, Chapter 7, Bouncing Balls, Macdonald, 1972.
Science, Models, and Toys, p.24, Chapter 3, Balls, Macdonald, 1974.

More to do

The Learning Through Science packs named below
contain the following cards that could be adapted for use
with slow learning children.

Sky and Space
Rockets and Spacecraft
3 2 1 Blast Off

Out of Doors
How Big?

BATTERIES AND BULBS

Contents

All children enjoy working with batteries and bulbs. This section is to help children with learning difficulties to find out for themselves about simple electric circuits and to use the knowledge they acquire. It suggests short practical investigations using batteries and bulbs to help children to understand the basic facts, and some of the dangers, of electricity. The assignments gradually become more complex so that the children's understanding of the work is extended and reinforced as it proceeds. However, teachers may prefer to do some of the work in a different order, or the children's questions may make it desirable to do so.

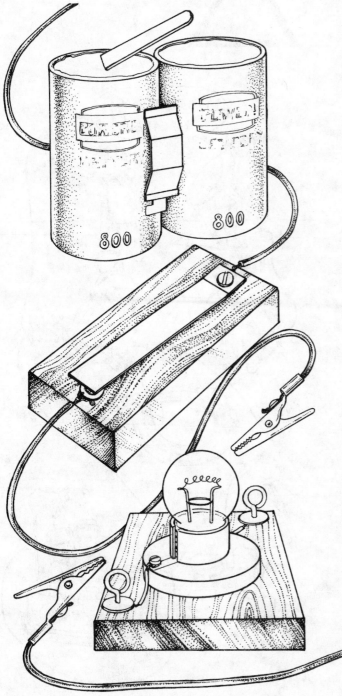

Information about apparatus

For the investigations with batteries and bulbs suggested in this section the children will need some simple apparatus. However, the items can easily be made and they will have a long and useful life in the classroom.

Time is well spent in making sturdy apparatus. Ramshackle constructions with loose connections give inconsistent and baffling results and are frustrating for children to use.

Many children can quite successfully help to make the equipment. Each pair of children will need the items below.

More equipment will be needed for extra children, but *not proportionately so*, as they are not all likely to be doing the same thing at any one time.

At the end of the section are: lists of items needed to make the wire leads, bulb boards and switches, page 105; directions for making this apparatus, page 105; the name and address of one supplier of electrical equipment, page 105.

Home-made items

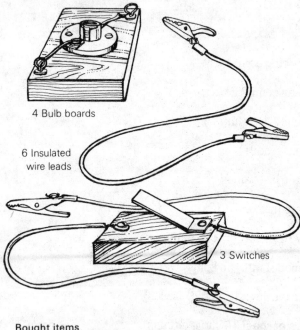

4 Bulb boards

6 Insulated wire leads

3 Switches

Bought items

5 MES (screw) bulbs, 2.5V, and 1 dud bulb

5 MES (screw) bulbholders

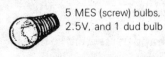

2 Bicycle headlight batteries, 3V, and 1 spent battery

Spare insulated wire

Safety

All work described in this unit is quite safe.
The batteries used are far too weak to give even the smallest shock.
But *make sure* that the children understand that

THEY MUST NEVER EXPERIMENT WITH MAINS ELECTRICITY WHICH IS ALWAYS DANGEROUS AND CAN BE LETHAL.

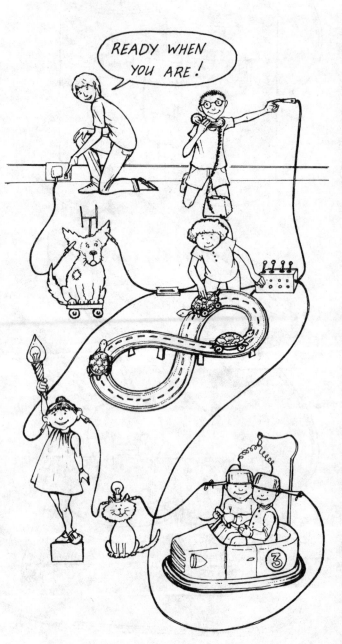

READY WHEN YOU ARE!

What do we need to light a bulb? How must these things be put together?

Electricity must have a complete continuous pathway, *a circuit*, if it is to light a bulb or to do any other work. Children need plenty of time to assimilate this idea.

For children to do
Find out how to light the bulb with this apparatus.

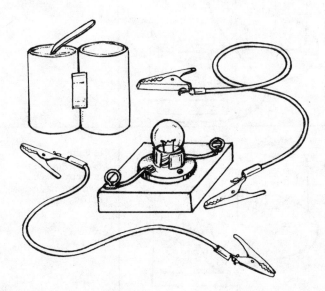

How many different ways of lighting the bulb can the children find?
Allow them plenty of time to talk about this and to try out their ideas.
Record each pattern by drawing, or by using gummed paper shapes as in the diagram.

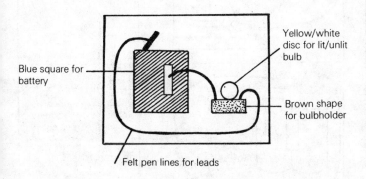

Blue square for battery

Yellow/white disc for lit/unlit bulb

Brown shape for bulbholder

Felt pen lines for leads

To discuss
All the patterns the children have found.
The things that are needed to light a bulb in a holder: a battery and two leads.
The idea of a continuous, complete pathway for the electricity from the battery, through a lead, through the bulb and through another lead back to the battery.
Encourage each child to trace this pathway with a finger. Point out its completeness when the bulb lights. Find the break if the bulb does not light. What happens if any of the connections are loose? Usually the bulb will not light, or it flickers when the apparatus is touched.

Lights out

This reinforces the idea of the basic electric circuit.

For children to do
Set up a circuit so that the bulb is lit. Without *damaging* the equipment, how many ways can the children find of *putting out* the light? Record each success by drawing or using gummed paper shapes. Then mend the circuit, so the bulb lights again.

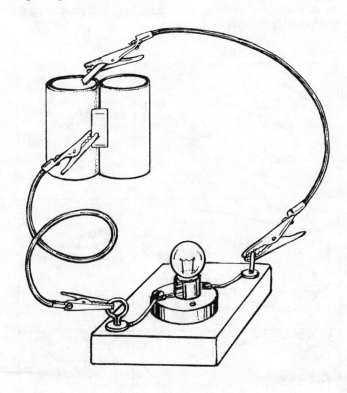

To discuss
Talk about why the bulb does not light in each case. Encourage the children to trace out the circuits and to point out any breaks.

Further work
Ask the children to light bulbs using different types of batteries. They will need to find two metal terminals on each type.

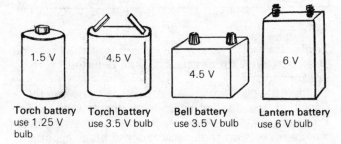

1.5 V	4.5 V	4.5 V	6 V
Torch battery use 1.25 V bulb	Torch battery use 3.5 V bulb	Bell battery use 3.5 V bulb	Lantern battery use 6 V bulb

Does the bulb light 1?

This activity, and the following one will show how well the children have understood what they have already done, and will give them more practical experiences.

For children to do
Give the children copies of *master sheet 1*, page 102. In the case of each illustration ask them to *predict* whether or not the bulb will light, and to *record that prediction* on the sheet. *Then* use their apparatus to *make up the pattern and test* their prediction practically.

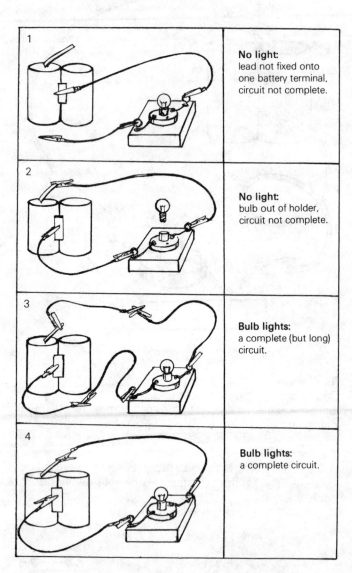

1

No light:
lead not fixed onto one battery terminal, circuit not complete.

2

No light:
bulb out of holder, circuit not complete.

3

Bulb lights:
a complete (but long) circuit.

4

Bulb lights:
a complete circuit.

To discuss
Talk over the children's predictions and why they were right or wrong.
Children are often anxious about predicting incorrectly. Encourage the idea that incorrect prediction is not *wrong*. Predicting the outcome of a test, then experimenting to find whether or not the prediction was correct, is an important part of the scientific way of working. An incorrect prediction merely means that one has to think again about the experiment or about one's reasoning.

Does the bulb light 2?

Master sheet 2, page 103, poses more problems.
Work in the same way, asking the children to record their prediction and then to test it practically.

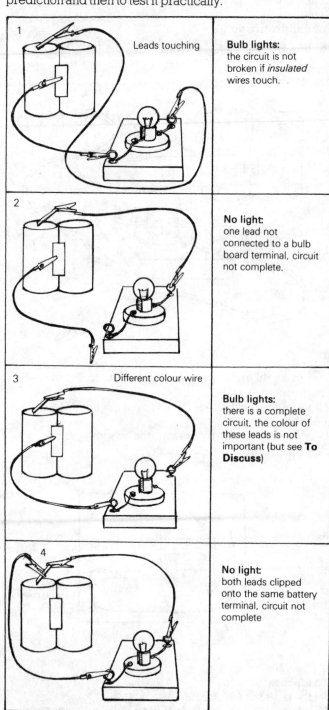

1   Leads touching

Bulb lights:
the circuit is not broken if *insulated* wires touch.

2

No light:
one lead not connected to a bulb board terminal, circuit not complete.

3   Different colour wire

Bulb lights:
there is a complete circuit, the colour of these leads is not important (but see **To Discuss**)

4

No light:
both leads clipped onto the same battery terminal, circuit not complete

To discuss
The predictions and the outcome of each pattern.
The significance of the colour of the wires (none with this apparatus, but the colour conventions used in *mains* wiring *are* important).

Further work
Similar sheets showing other kinds of battery could be prepared and used.

Lighting a loose bulb

This shows how the circuit is continuous through a bulb.

For children to do
If the children do not discover that one lead must touch the small knob at the base of the stem and the other lead must touch the metal stem, question them to help them to find out.

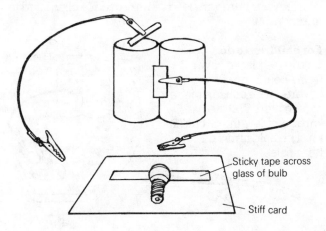

Sticky tape across glass of bulb

Stiff card

To discuss
The continuity of the circuit within the bulb. Show the children a bulb you have dismantled. To do this, gently remove the glass with pliers.
Reasons for using bulb holders.

Very thin wire which lights up

Two thicker supporting wires held apart by a glass bead

One thicker wire extends to metal knob at base of stem

Other wire is soldered onto the side

Further work
1. Examine a loose bulb holder to see how the stem and base of the bulb connect with parts of the bulb holder.

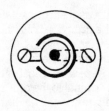
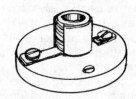

Knob at base of bulb touches metal at base of bulbholder which connects to one screw

The other screw connects to the metal holder which the bulb screws into

2. Look at other kinds of light bulb. Find the terminals, discuss bulb holders.

Remember that mains electricity is dangerous.

What does a switch do?

A switch is a way of breaking or completing a circuit.

For children to do
Show the children a home-made switch.
Before they put it into a circuit, ask how they think it will work.

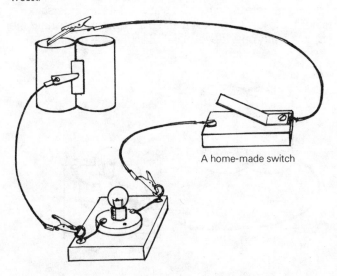

A home-made switch

At first there is no light. Press the switch, the bulb lights. Release the switch, the light goes out. Does the same thing happen when the switch is put on the other side of the bulb?

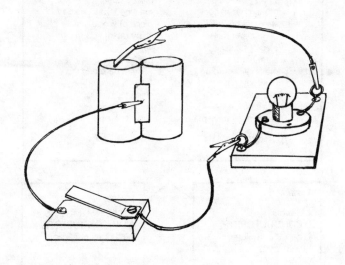

To discuss
The structure of a switch. The effect it has of completing or breaking a circuit.
If the children are interested, you might look at the way some bought switches operate.

Remember to remind them *never* to take the top off a switch in a mains circuit.

If children are interested in flashing Morse messages, you will find the Morse code on page 80.

Conductors and insulators

This allows children to sort out for themselves two important sets of materials concerned with electricity: conductors and insulators. All metals conduct electricity. Most other materials do not.

For children to do
Try to complete the circuit by using different objects and materials to join terminals A and B. It is important to hold the objects firmly onto the terminals. Display the results.

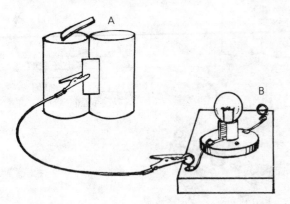

Try:	
string	rubber band
metal coat hanger	plastic ruler
shiny metal fork	drinking straw
large clean nail	piece of wood
piece of card	shiny metal spoon
aluminium foil	key
piece of recording tape	pvc insulated wire
painted tin lid	with bare ends
pair of scissors	with covered ends
glass bottle	shiny tin can
china or pottery plate	knitting needle
	strand of wool

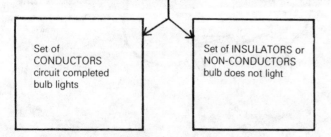

Set of CONDUCTORS circuit completed bulb lights	Set of INSULATORS or NON-CONDUCTORS bulb does not light

To discuss
The objects in the sets and the materials they are made of. Try to establish that the things which completed the circuit and lit the bulb were all made of metal.
What is a metal? Hard, shiny, can be bent without breaking, makes ringing sound when tapped.
Discuss the materials which do not conduct electricity: plastic, rubber, wood, paper, paint, glass, china. Why is it important to know which materials are electrical insulators? They allow us to control electricity.

Bare wires and short circuits

Bare wires conduct electricity very well, but short circuits easily occur. These are dangerous in mains circuits. When children have found out about short circuits, they should also be avoided in this kind of work as they run down batteries very quickly.
Experiments in 2 and 3 below will be easier for children to do if they use bare wire leads with crocodile clips fitted to the ends.

For children to do
1. Strip the plastic cover from about 20 cm PVC covered wire or use a piece of bare wire. Will the bare wire complete the circuit? It must be held firmly onto the terminals.

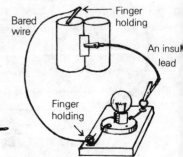

2. Try two bare wire leads.

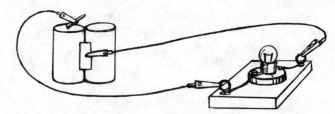

3. Bare wires touch. What happens if the wires touch?

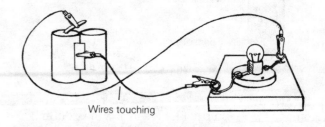

Wires touching

To discuss
1. Bare wires complete the circuit just as well as insulated wires, but if they touch each other the light goes out, the battery/bulb circuit is broken.
When there is a direct connection between the two terminals of the battery the bulb is by-passed. Most of the electricity *floods* from one battery terminal to the other, and such a small amount reaches the bulb that it will not light. This is a *short circuit*.
A short circuit quickly flattens a battery. It also generates a lot of heat and may cause a fire in a mains circuit. This is one of the dangers of worn or perished cables or flexes.

2. How might bare wires be insulated? Consider some of the materials and objects the children have found to be insulators.
Try threading a bare wire through a straw, wrapping it in insulating tape, or other ideas the children have.

More short circuits

If the children have understood the previous page without difficulty they may be interested in three more examples which will reinforce their learning about circuits.

For children to do
Predict what will happen in each of the following cases, then test to find out.

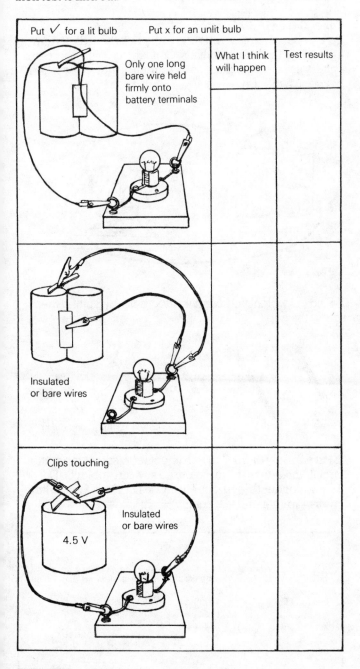

Put ✓ for a lit bulb Put x for an unlit bulb	What I think will happen	Test results
Only one long bare wire held firmly onto battery terminals		
Insulated or bare wires		
Clips touching Insulated or bare wires 4.5 V		

To discuss
The reasons for the short circuits in the three patterns. Ask the children to trace out the circuit in each case from one battery terminal to the other.
Can the children think what will happen if insulated wire is used in step 1? The bulb still will not light, but in this case because the battery is not included in the circuit. This is not a short circuit.

Switches and short circuits

You may prefer not to introduce these possibilities if the children have found the work on short circuits difficult to follow.

For children to do
Ask if a switch will still work if it is put: 1. between the battery terminals; 2. between the bulb terminals.

Test to find out.

1.

2.

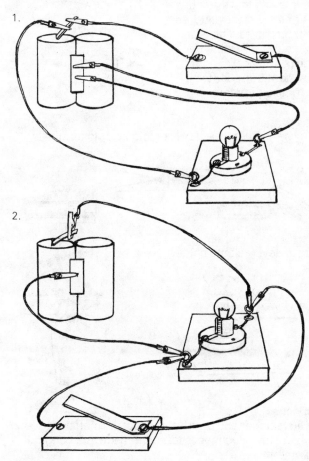

To discuss
In both cases the following happens.

Switch attached *remains* alight Because the switch does not break the bulb battery circuit

Switch depressed goes out Because there is now a short circuit, an alternative pathway from one battery terminal to the other which allows the bulb to be by-passed

Switch released lights again Because the short circuit is broken and the normal one operates again

Devising equipment

Children enjoy devising and making their own apparatus. It encourages imaginative thinking and manipulative skills.

For children to do

1. Show the children how to fix a crocodile clip to a lead. Loosen the screw, do not remove it, slip the wire underneath, looping round the same way that the screw will tighten. Let the children do it themselves. This is an important and worthwhile piece of practical *know-how*. It applies to all electrical equipment.

2. Devise another way of connecting leads to terminals.

Try:

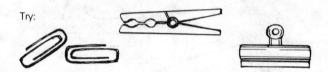

3. Try to devise a bulb holder.

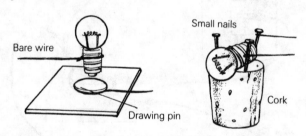

Bare wire

Drawing pin

Small nails

Cork

To discuss

The advantages and disadvantages of the methods used. Compare the effectiveness of home-made and bought equipment.

Further work

1. What other ways are there of connecting wires to make circuits? Look at examples of plugs and sockets.

Danger do not push bare wires into sockets; do not touch the pins of a plug not fully pushed home.

2. Must it be the end of a wire that connects with the terminal? There is a circuit and the bulb will light, but the trailing end is electrically *live* and would be dangerous on mains apparatus.

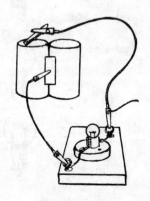

Clean connections

When metallic articles do not conduct it is usually because their outside layers have become coated with a compound formed between the metal and gases in the air. Thus the outside layer is not pure metal. Such a compound can often be seen as a discolouration or dullness, but it is not always noticeable. It can easily be cleaned off with fine sandpaper. Grease and dirt are also insulators.

For children to do

Fix another screw eye into one of the bulb boards, 2-3 cm from one of the bulb terminals. Connect the bulb board to a battery as in the diagram, so the circuit is broken by a gap between two screw eyes.

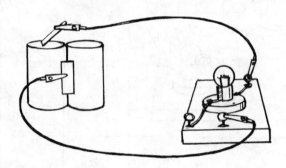

1. Find out which nails conduct electricity by putting them across the gap.

Rusty   Painted   Greasy   Dirty   Clean and bright

2. Put a variety of small metal objects across the gap in the circuit. *Include* rusty, discoloured and dirty objects. Do they all conduct electricity? If any do not clean them with fine sandpaper and test again.

Try:		
coin	paper-clip	perforated zinc
bulldog clip	key ring	discs of different metals
key	painted tin lid (both sides)	plastic covered hair grips

To discuss

Electrical connections must be *clean* and *firm*. All metals conduct electricity provided they are bright and shiny.

*Set of metal discs, 3 each of 8 magnetic and non-magnetic metals, 24 in the set. From E. J. Arnold. Catalogue Number SW172.

Trouble shooting

This exercise reminds children of what they have already learnt and gives them a check list to use when they find a fault in one of their electrical models.

For children to do
Show the children a problem circuit which incorporates *one* fault. Ask them what may be wrong. Get them to test their ideas including the substitution of good batteries and bulbs if dud ones are suspected.

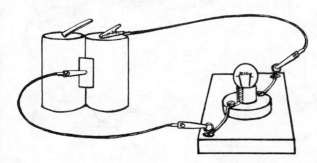

Build up a list of possible faults as below.

The bulb will not light because
The circuit is not complete
Bare wires are touching, short circuit
Wires or clips are loose
Battery is flat
Switch is not on
Bulb is dud
Bulb is loose
There is a dirty connection
Something is blocking the connection
Wire not stripped of insulation

Use the list to try to solve some real problems.

1. Bicycle not used for several snowy weeks. The lamp will not work. What is wrong? (Battery probably flat or terminals corroded.)

2. Torch flickers, the light sometimes on, sometimes off. What is wrong? (Bulb probably loose or spring in the base is weak.)

3. Pocket calculator will not work. (Bit of paper stuck in battery terminals.)

Further work
Pairs of children could make up faulty circuits for each other to *trouble shoot* and discover what is wrong.

Light a model

Making an electrically lit model will test the children's understanding of the work they have done.

For children to do
Encourage the children to work out their own plans.

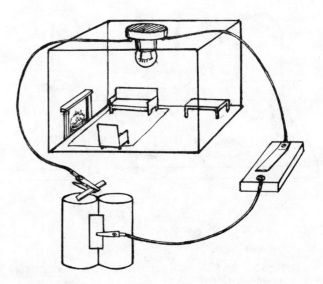

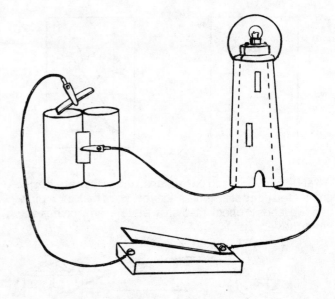

What do they need? For the electrical part they need a bulb holder, a bulb, a battery, a switch, insulated wire; and for the model? What will they do? How will they fix the bulb holder, or secure the wire? If the light does not work when the model is made start trouble shooting.

To discuss
The children's designs, could they be improved?

Electrical games

For children to do

1. Make a steady hand tester. Connect to a battery. What happens when the wire loop touches the track? Each player sees how far he can pass the loop along the track without letting the two touch.

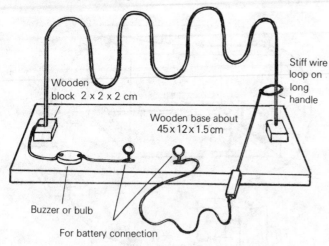

Stiff wire track e.g. coat hanger

Wooden block 2 x 2 x 2 cm

Stiff wire loop on long handle

Wooden base about 45 x 12 x 1.5 cm

Buzzer or bulb

For battery connection

2. Make a quiz board. Use stiff card, 20 x 30 cm. Measure, mark and make 5 to 10 pairs of holes. Push a brass paper fastener through each hole and open out. Connect pairs together with insulated wire, wrapping bared ends securely round the opened ends of the fasteners.

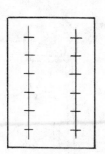
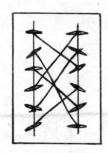

Arrange questions and correct answers so they are beside connected pairs of fasteners. Players use a battery, a bulb and two leads to check their answers. The light comes on when they are right.

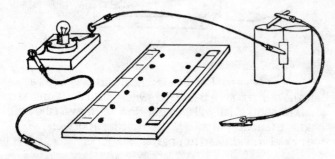

To discuss

The way the circuit is completed in each game.

More than one in a circuit

When two or more bulbs are in a single circuit they are said to be arranged in series.

For children to do

Ask the children to make up a circuit including a bulb and a switch.

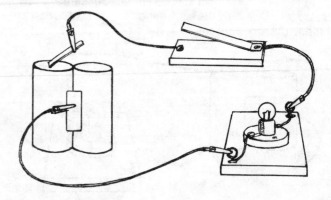

Now challenge them to find a way of using another battery to light two bulbs. They are most likely to make a series circuit, as shown below. Any other arrangement which works will have parallel circuits. In that case go on to page 101 and return to this pattern later.

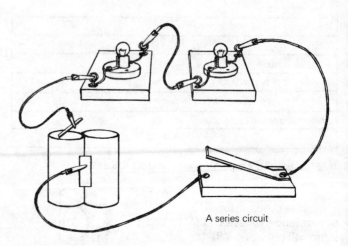

A series circuit

When two bulbs are in series do they both light up when the switch is pressed? Are the two bulbs each as bright as when there is only one in a circuit? Compare the bulbs in the two circuits shown above. *Master sheet 3*, page 104, shows more variations for the children to try.

To discuss

This is a single circuit, so any break in it will affect all the bulbs in the circuit. When one bulb is removed (or breaks) all the bulbs will go out. Whenever a switch is put in a series circuit, it controls all the lights in that circuit. The battery is designed to give a certain amount of power to each circuit that is connected to it. The more bulbs in a series circuit, the less bright each one will be.

Two circuits from one battery

This is another way to use one battery to light two or more bulbs. These bulbs are said to be arranged in parallel.

For children to do
Ask the children to make a simple circuit including a bulb and a switch. Challenge them to add another circuit to the same battery.

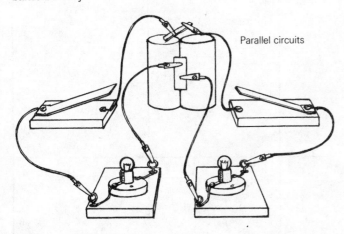

Parallel circuits

1. What happens when one switch is pressed? When the other switch is pressed? When both switches are pressed? Are the bulbs equally bright?

2. Are the two lit bulbs the same brightness as two lit in series? See page 100.

3. What happens if one bulb is unscrewed and removed? Does the other one still light when it is switched on?

4. Can you light three bulbs from one battery in this way?

To discuss
Each bulb has its own separate circuit. Therefore it is not affected by the removal of a bulb from the other circuit, or by the switch of that circuit. As each bulb is in its own circuit it receives power independently of the other circuit, therefore the brightness of the light is the same for each bulb. However, more power is being used and the battery will not last as long. This is another way in which parallel circuits can be arranged.

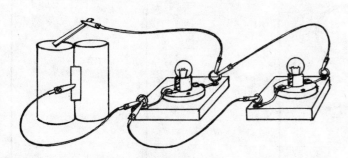

Would it be better to wire two bulbs in parallel or in series in a model? Why?

A model with two lights

For children to do
The children could now make models which incorporate two lights, two lights in a model room, headlamps on a toy lorry, a robot with two eyes.

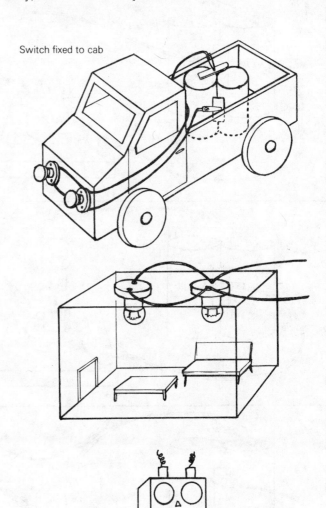

Switch fixed to cab

As with the earlier model (page 99) encourage the children to make their own plans. What do they need? What will they do first? Show them how bought miniature switches can be used to allow lights to be left switched on.

To discuss
The children's designs, possible improvements. What will happen to each model if one of the bulbs blows?

Master Sheet 1

NAME

Put ✓ for a lit bulb Put x for an unlit bulb	What I think will happen	Test results
1 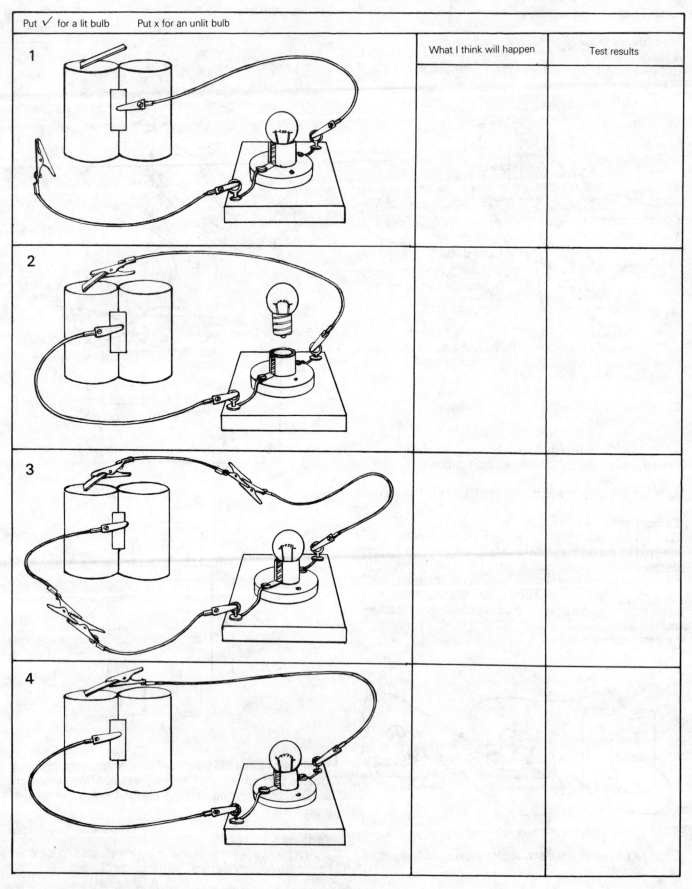		
2		
3		
4		

Master Sheet 2

NAME

Put ✓ for a lit bulb Put x for an unlit bulb	What I think will happen	Test results
1 Leads touching		
2		
3 Different colour wire		
4		

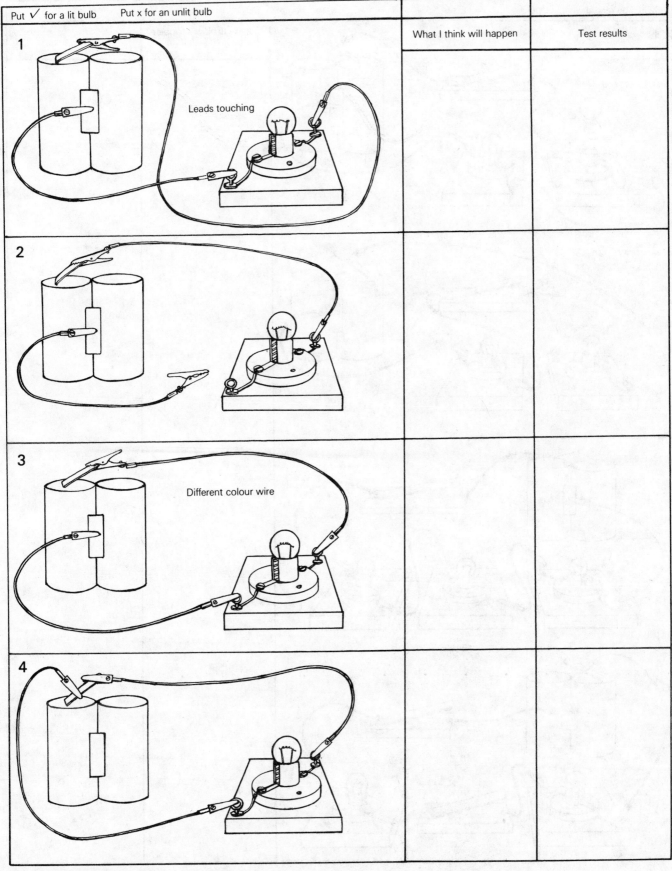

NAME

Switch on record what happens	What I think will happen when I switch on	Test results
1		
2		
3		
4		

Items needed to make the apparatus in this section

Wood, screws, etc.

softwood blocks, about 10 x 10 cm at least 1 cm thick
for bulb boards – not plywood or chipboard, which will not take screws

softwood blocks, 5 x 10 cm 1 cm thick
for home-made switches

screws, ½" No. 4 round headed
for fixing bulb holders to boards and models

screws ½" No. 6 round headed, shiny metal
for making switches

screw eyes, shiny metal 1 cm diameter loop
as used for curtain wire, for bulb boards

washers, shiny metal, to fit thread of screw eyes
to clamp wire firmly to screw eyes

springy steel banding
for making switches – try a local factory or packing firm *or use* metal draught-excluder strip

Electrical equipment

The following items may be bought from many suppliers. One speedy and reliable firm, whose catalogue numbers are listed below, is R.S. Components, PO Box 427, 13-17 Epworth Street, London EC2P 2HA. Telephone 01 253 3040 or 01 250 3131.

MES bulb holders
6 for bulb boards, 10 for models: usually sold in packs (RSC: MES battenholders, pack of 5, black, 564-891)

round MES bulbs, 2.5 volt and 3.5 volt
for bulb board and models (RSC: round MES bulbs, 2.5 V pack of 10, 586-144, 3.5 V pack of 10, 586-166)

crocodile clips
for leads, switches and models (RSC: crocodile clips (standard) 423-021, pack of 20)

reel copper wire, 24 swg, approx 0.5 mm diameter*
(RSC: tinned copper wire, 24 swg 355-085, 200 g reel)

reel PVC insulated wire
(RSC: extra flexible wire 25 m reel: black, 356-167; red, 356-173; green, 357-075; blue, 357-069; yellow, 357-081)

bought switches
for models, buy locally

cycle lamp batteries, type 800, 3.0 V
for tests and models, buy locally

*This item is needed only for the work on pages 96 and 97; PVC covered wire, stripped of its insulation, may be used instead. Secondary schools are often willing to supply a short length of copper wire.

Instructions for making apparatus

Tools needed
saw
sandpaper
screwdriver
bradawl
tin snips
wire strippers – the cheapest and most efficient is a Bib
metal drill
file

Two important points about making electrical connections

1. Only *loosen* the small screws on the apparatus until the wire can be slipped underneath. Do not take the screws right out; they are difficult to put back.

2. Always loop the wire *Clockwise* around the screw; tightening the screw pulls the wire firmly around it.

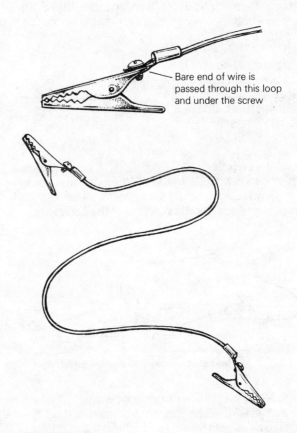

Bare end of wire is passed through this loop and under the screw

To make wire leads
Cut pieces of insulated wire, most about 20 cm long, a few about 30 cm.
Strip about 1.5 cm of the plastic covering from both ends of each piece of wire. If you are using multiflex wire, twist the strands together.
Fix a crocodile clip to each bared end by passing through the loop and under the screw.

To make a bulb board

Use a softwood block, not plywood or chipboard which will not take screws. To avoid splitting the wood, start each screw hole with a bradawl.

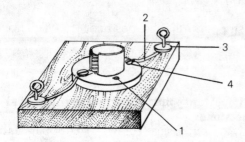

1. Screw the bulb holder to the centre of the block of wood.

2. Cut short lengths of insulated wire to join the screw terminals on the base of the bulb holder to the screw eyes. Strip the insulation from the ends of the pieces of wire.

3. Fit one end of each piece of wire on to the thread of a screw eye between two shiny washers, and screw the eye firmly into place.

4. Slip the other ends of the wires clockwise beneath the loosened screws of the terminals of the bulb holder. Screw down firmly.

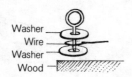

To make a switch

Springy band switches are best. When they are released batteries are automatically disconnected. Use softwood blocks. Start each wood screw hole with a bradawl.

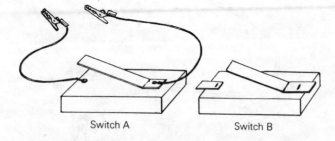

Switch A is made with packing case banding. The brass strip terminals of old batteries can be used in the same way.
1. Cut the band with tin snips. File down sharp edges.
2. For the screw hole in the metal, make a start dent with a hammer and nail, then use a metal drill.
3. Strip the insulation from the ends of 2 short lengths of wire (10-15 cm). Fix the band and wire to the wood with *round headed shiny metal screws.*
4. Fix crocodile clips to the other ends of the wires.

Switch B is made with draught excluder strip, which is fixed onto the wood with a staple gun.

More to do

The Learning Through Science pack named below contains material that could be adapted for use with slow learning children.

Electricity

Many of the cards in this pack would be relevant.

A CUP OF TEA

Making a cup of tea is an excellent starting point for scientific investigations. Many questions may be asked about the different activities that are involved, and answered by practical experiments. The enquiries which are proposed in this section will help children with learning difficulties to think critically about everyday activities, and to devise fair tests to assess the processes involved in them.

Contents

*Boiling water must be used in these investigations.
†A pot of tea is needed *to start* these investigations. It is not necessary to use boiling water in the rest of this work.

107

Making a cup of tea

This introductory activity is for teacher and children to do together. The children should be encouraged to do as much of it as they safely can.

The work helps children to put a sequence of operations into the correct order, and to distinguish essential steps from the rest. It also provides the setting for discussions about the dangers which are involved in making tea. These are taken up again on page 109.

For children to do

1. Discuss with the children the things that are needed if a cup of tea is to be made for everybody in the group. How many people? So how many cups, saucers, kettles, teapots? How much milk and tea? Collect together all the necessary articles.

Tea

Sugar

2. Make the tea and pour it out. Talk through the steps in the process as they occur.

3. Show the children how to build up a flow chart showing the sequence of operations. This could be done in words or in pictures. It could be completed by individual children, or by a group.

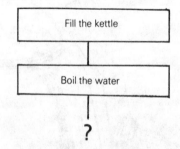

Fill the kettle

Boil the water

?

To discuss

If the children worked separately, compare their charts. Are they all the same? Did anybody forget anything? Talk about the *order* of the operations, try to help the children to sort out the right order of essential steps in making tea. What did I (you) do next? *Must* that be done next? Would it matter if I (you) did not do that at all? Discuss whether the same result could be achieved with different equipment. Must the water be boiled in a kettle? Ask the children how tea is made in their homes. Teabag in a cup? Tea made in a saucepan? Other ways.?

Different kinds of tea

This kind of work teaches children how to observe things scientifically, by using *all* appropriate senses to gather information. An important point about comparison is that it involves looking for *similarities* as well as differences.

For children to do

1. Make a collection of different kinds of tea.

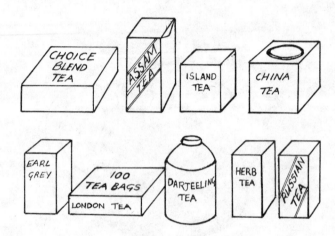

Compare the tea samples. Look for similarities as well as differences. What do they look like? Do they all smell the same? Do they feel different? How do they taste? Try to make 2 or 3 kinds, according to the directions on the packets. What else can be found out about them? Read the writing on the packets.

2. Ask the children to bring empty tea packets from home. Make a display. Compare the information on the packets, the amount of tea, any instructions for using it, where it was grown or packed, the name of the tea merchant; anything else?

To discuss

Talk about what tea is and where it comes from. What sort of things might contribute to differences in taste: different varieties of tea plant, growth in different countries, the addition of other things like oil of bergamot or scented flowers.

Why are teas named as they are, after people, or places? What other kinds of tea are there? Mint tea, camomile tea and others. Perhaps try some of these if the children are interested.

Boiling water

Many children use boiling water at home, and serious accidents sometimes occur. A lot of teachers feel it important to use activities such as these to show children the dangers of boiling water, and to help them to understand how to handle it safely. The teacher's help is needed for all the work below, children should not do it on their own.

For children to do

Discuss with the children different ways of boiling water, electric kettle, kettle on gas ring, saucepan on fire.

1. *Boiling water in an electric kettle.* How should an electric kettle be used? Water must cover the element before the kettle is switched on. How far can it be filled? Look inside to see. Watch a *boiling* kettle. Steam scalds, so kettle spouts and holes in their lids should point away from people.

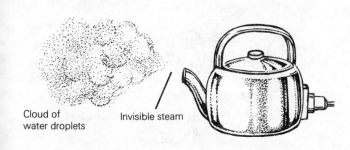

Cloud of water droplets   Invisible steam

2. *How do we know when water is boiling?* If possible, allow children to watch water in a saucepan come to the boil, then boil vigorously. How should the handle of the saucepan be placed? Refer back to the question of how full a kettle should be, or any container in which water is boiled.

3. *How can we use boiling water safely?* Fill an electric kettle with cold water and act through the process of making and pouring tea. Include dangerous things which are commonly done, such as carrying the kettle of *boiling* water across the room. Ask the children to watch carefully and to point out any dangers they notice. With the children, work out some safety rules:
do not carry a kettle of boiling water, take the tea pot to the kettle;
take the cups to the teapot;
put the cup on a table while the hot liquid is poured into it, do not hold it;
see that small children are not playing nearby where water might spill on them or where they might pull a tablecloth.

How hot is hot?

For some of the activities in this section children will need to measure temperatures. The investigations on this page will help them to understand the temperature scale, and will give them practice in using thermometers. Master sheets of thermometer outlines which may be useful when children are learning to read thermometers are in Weather records, pages 127 and 128.

For children to do
Ask the children to use thermometers to find the temperature of some of the things below. Record each temperature separately on a copy of the appropriate master sheet. Remind the children to *leave the thermometer in the liquid while reading the temperature.* Let them find out what happens if it is taken out.

Cold   Hot

Iced water

Cup of tea freshly made   Cup of tea cold enough to drink

Washing up water

To discuss
Talk about the temperature readings. Try to get the children to understand that the higher the reading, the hotter the liquid. Use the common adjectives that describe temperatures: hot, hotter, hottest, warm, cool, cold. Discuss how things can be made cooler. Will water which has been standing in the room for several hours be the same temperature as the air in the room? Test to find out.

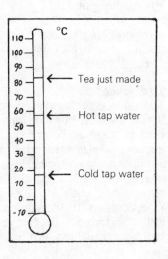

°C

← Tea just made

← Hot tap water

← Cold tap water

Must tea be made with boiling water? A fair test

Devising and using fair tests is fundamental to science. When a pot of tea is made many things may vary: the amount of tea used, the type of teapot, the volume of water added, the time it is left to brew. These are variables. To find out how changing one of these variables affects the tea, all the rest must be kept unchanged. This experiment introduces this important idea to the children. On later pages of this section it is suggested that children should devise their own fair tests.

For children to do
Ask whether the water must be *boiling* if good tea is to be made. Mrs Beeton wrote "in order to make good tea it is necessary that the water should be quite boiling". Do modern cookery books give tea-making instructions? How can we find out for ourselves whether boiling water makes a difference? Do a test. Use identical transparent heat-proof containers, such as 500 cc Pyrex jugs, so the children can see what happens. Put one heaped teaspoon of loose tea into each jug.

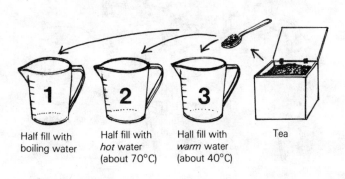

1	2	3	
Half fill with boiling water	Half fill with *hot* water (about 70°C)	Hall fill with *warm* water (about 40°C)	Tea

Let each jug brew for 3 minutes. Use a kitchen timer. Watch the jugs as the tea is brewing. What happens to the tea leaves? Strain the brews and pour back into the jugs. Compare the colours of the brews against the light. Add 1 tablespoonful of milk to each jug. Compare the colours of the brews again. Compare their tastes.

To discuss
The four sets of observations the children have made, do they answer the question for which this test was devised? *Is* it important to use boiling water to make tea? Talk about the importance of tests being fair, if their results are to give sensible answers to questions. Take the children through this fair test: same amount of tea in each jug; same kind of tea in each; same amount of water; brewed for the same time; compared in the same way. The only thing to change is the thing whose effect we want to know about, the temperature of the water.

Teapots

This will help children to appreciate the variety of materials and range of designs which may be used for an everyday object, and to consider whether they are equally fit for their purpose. This is continued on the next page.

For children to do
1. Collect and display as many teapots as possible. Sort them in different ways: according to size, according to material, according to shape.

2. What do people think makes a good teapot? To find out, make a survey. List the things the children think people might consider important. These might include: how much the pot holds, how heavy it is, how long it keeps the tea warm, how well it pours, how comfortable the handle, how attractive the design, how easy to clean, how well the lid stays on when pouring tea. Ask parents and teachers to say which *two things* they think most important in a teapot.

To discuss
Talk over the children's sorting activities, discuss the teapots in the collection.
Sort out the results of the survey. Do two or three things emerge as outstandingly important? Can the children think why these things were chosen by so many people?

Metal or pottery teapot?

The advantages of the different materials teapots are made from is one of the questions likely to be raised by the survey suggested on the previous page. Metal and pottery teapots are common, but *any two materials could be compared*, or more could be included. The children should be encouraged to help to devise a fair test.

For children to do

Ask which the children think will keep tea hot longer, a metal or a pottery pot. How could we find out? How to do a fair test? Choose teapots of *the same size*. Use hot water to represent tea; it need not be boiling, a starting temperature of 65-70°C will do. Fill both pots with water at the *same temperature*. Record the starting temperature of the water, then its temperature in both pots at the *same intervals*.

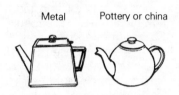

Metal   Pottery or china

Metal pot	Temperature of water	Pottery pot
°C	Before into pot	°C
	After 5 min. in pot	
	After 10 min. in pot	
	After 15 min. in pot	

Lids which will hold thermometers can be made easily.

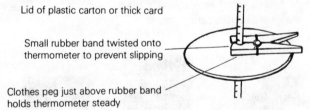

Lid of plastic carton or thick card

Small rubber band twisted onto thermometer to prevent slipping

Clothes peg just above rubber band holds thermometer steady

To discuss

Compare the two sets of readings.
Which pot of *tea* was the cooler after 15 minutes. Which the warmer? So which is the better pot for keeping the tea hot? Talk this over with the children, try to make sure that they understand how to draw the right conclusion from the thermometer readings.
Discuss other differences between metal and pottery pots. How heavy they are when they are empty, and when they are full. Compare them. Consider how easily they break if they are dropped. Which material do the children think they would choose if they had to buy a metal or a pottery teapot? Why?

*See master sheets of thermometer outlines, Weather records, pages 127 and 128.

Warming the pot

We do some things without thinking about them at all. For instance, in some homes the teapot is always warmed before the tea is made. Why? This enquiry encourages children to question and assess the usefulness of common procedures. It helps them to develop an enquiring mind.

For children to do

Talk about warming the pot. In how many of the children's homes is this done? Why is it done? Does it make any difference to the heat of the tea? How could we find out? Help the children to devise a test. *Either* use two identical teapots, preferably china or pottery, *or* use the same pot, *first* cold, then warmed. The water need not be boiling, a starting temperature of 60-70 °C will do, although the children may wish to follow on with a real test with boiling water and tea.
Make a record of the temperature of the cooling water. A kitchen timer helps to get the intervals right.

Cold pot   Warmed pot
(hot water   (hot water
added)   added)

Cold pot	Temperature of water	Warmed pot
°C	Before into pot	°C
	After 5 min. in pot	
	After 10 min. in pot	
	After 15 min. in pot	

To discuss

Talk over the results of the test. Do they answer the question? Is it worth warming the pot? When hot water is put into a cold pot some of its heat is taken up at once by the pot, so tea made in a cold pot will be cooler than if it were made in a warm one. If the children have made tea in their test, discuss whether warming the pot makes a difference to the taste of the tea. The amount of heat taken up by a cold pot depends on the material the pot is made of. Metal pots are very common, and children may be interested to compare them with pottery or china pots. The results of the test adjacent may show this. Is it as important to warm a metal pot?
This work could lead on to discussions about cups, mugs and beakers. How well do they keep drinks hot? Do some get too hot to hold? Test to find out.**

*See master sheets of thermometer outlines, *Weather records* pages 127 and 128.
**Learning Through Science, *Materials*, the card *Cups, Mugs and Beakers*, Macdonald, 1982.

How much tea?

Some children might find it easier to compare only two samples, say a brew made with one teaspoon of tea with one made from three teaspoons. The strength test works perfectly well if water at 60-70 °C is used, but if the children are to compare the tastes, as suggested at the end of the test, the teas must be made with boiling water.

For children to do
Does more tea make a stronger brew?
Use identical transparent heat-proof containers, such as 500 cc Pyrex jugs. See the note above about the temperature of the water.

One heaped teaspoon of tea

Two heaped teaspoons of tea

Three heaped teaspoons of tea

Encourage the children to help to devise a fair test. How much water shall we use? Must we fill each jug to the same mark? Must we leave to brew for the same length of time, say 3 minutes? Get rid of the tea leaves. How? Strain then pour back into the glass jugs.

Stand the jugs on a window sill or hold them up to the light in some other way. Compare the colours of the brews. Does the colour tell us anything about the strength of each brew? The containers must be identical, so that the *thickness* of the liquids being compared is the same, another aspect of a fair test.

If boiling water has been used, add the same amount of milk to each brew and compare their tastes.

To discuss
The results of the test. *Does* more tea make a stronger brew? Talk about the rule of thumb method, 'one (spoon) for each person and one for the pot'. Does this seem reasonable in the light of the test?
Is it always the case that solutions become steadily stronger, the more solid is added? Think about coffee and salt. This might lead directly to the work on page 115.

If the children noticed that they got much less tea from the 3 teaspoons brew than from the one made with 1 teaspoon of tea leaves, they might like to find out more about the absorbency of tea leaves.

Teabags

For children to do
1. In how many of the children's homes are teabags used? Why not use a loose tea? Does a teabag make a better brew than loose tea? Can the children devise their own test? An important first step is to find how much tea is in a teabag. Cut one open and find how many teaspoons of tea are in it.

Now compare one teabag and the same amount of loose tea. For the test to be fair use the same kind of tea, the same volume of water, at the same temperature, brew for the same time. The only difference should be teabag/loose tea.

Strain the brews, pour back into the jugs, compare the colours. Add the same amount of milk to each and compare the tastes.

2. What kind of material makes a good teabag? Look at some teabags. Decide what is important about the fabric a teabag is made of. Collect together some materials which seem suitable. Make some teabags and test them. How well do they let the tea brew, keep in the tea leaves, survive in hot water without disintegrating?

To discuss
1. In the light of the results of the test talk again about the advantages of teabags: no straining needed, no tea leaves to get rid of, tea can be made in a cup. What are the advantages of loose tea: better flavour, less wasteful? Costs might also be compared.

2. Discuss teabag fabrics. Which did the children find best? Why? You may think it worth following up the popular idea that the tea in teabags contains a lot of dust. Is this true? Sieve teabag tea and loose tea, compare quantities of leaves and dust. Remember that there is always a lot of dust in the bottom of a packet of loose tea.

Brewing the tea

For children to do

1. Ask how long tea must be left to brew. How does time affect strength?

Add one teaspoon of tea to each transparent jug. Pour in hot water at 60-70 °C. How much into each jug? Leave jug 1 for 1 minute, jug 2 for 2 minutes, jug 3 for 4 minutes.

In each case pour the tea through a strainer and back into the jug. Hold the jugs up to the light. Compare the colours of the brews. Add 1 tablespoon of milk to each jug and compare the colours again.

2. Does stirring the tea help it to brew? This is done in many households. How can we test? Pour hot water onto 1 teaspoon of tea in each jug. Leave for 4 minutes.

Do not stir	Stir every minute

Strain off the tea leaves. Compare the colours.

To discuss

Talk over the results of the tests. What helps the tea to brew? How do these conclusions fit in with the instructions on the packets? Are brewing times recommended? Discuss the effect of time on other things. Hot things get cooler, very cold things warmer (ice melts). Changes in cooking: eggs go runny then harder, then hard; vegetables may be underdone or overcooked; colours fade.

Tea cosies

This enquiry introduces children to the idea of insulation against loss of heat, and to some of the materials used for this purpose.

For children to do

Discuss the purpose of tea cosies. Are they used in the children's homes? How well do they work? Choose a large teapot. Make a lid to hold a thermometer. Fill the pot with hot water, at least 60°C.

Measure the temperature of the water in the pot, after 5 minutes, after 10 minutes, after 15 minutes. Record as below. Empty the pot. Let it get quite cold. Now repeat the test, but with a cosy over the pot. Can the children think what they must do to make the comparison between the two pots fair? They must start with a *cold* pot, use water at the same temperature, use the same volume of water, record the water temperature at the same intervals.

No tea cosy	Temperature of water	With a cosy
* 100 90 80 70 60 50 40 30 20 10 0 -10 °C	Before into pot After 5 min. in pot After 10 min. in pot After 15 min. in pot	100 90 80 70 60 50 40 30 20 10 0 -10 °C

To discuss

Compare the two sets of readings. Is it a good idea to use a tea cosy? Talk about the way insulating materials prevent heat from escaping. Other examples in the home include lagging on hot water pipes and tanks, roof insulation, cavity wall insulation, clothing and bed covers.**

What sort of materials are used for these things? The children might like to design, make and test their own tea cosy. As well as usual materials, test tea cosies made of things used for other kinds of insulation: crumpled newspaper, polystyrene. Which is the most efficient?

*See master sheets of thermometer outlines in *Weather records*, pages 127 and 128.
**See *Me and my clothes*, pages 29-52.

Separating tea from tea leaves

Decanting, straining and filtering are three ways of separating liquids from solids.

For children to do

Ask if they use tea strainers at home. Why? Check what happens. Make a pot of tea using either hot (60-70°C) or boiling water and loose tea. Let it stand for at least 3 minutes.

1. Now pour some of the tea into a transparent jug or jar. Are there any tea leaves in the jug? Where are most of the tea leaves? Look in the pot.

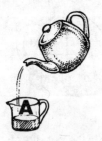 

2. Pour some of the tea in the pot through a strainer into another transparent container. Compare. What does the strainer do?

Not strained   Strained

3. Pour *half* the strained tea through a filter made of blotting paper or filter paper into another transparent container. Compare. Is there anything on the filter?

Strained   Filtered

To discuss

Talk about the way most of the tea leaves are left in the pot when the tea is poured. If the children watched tea brewing with boiling water (page 110) they may remember seeing the leaves settle. When tea is poured off the leaves it is decanted.

Straining removes the remaining tea leaves. What are the advantages in getting rid of these? Look at several strainers, how big is the mesh? What will they let through? Some teapots have their own built-in strainer, a mesh or series of holes across the base of the spout. Is this common? Examine the pots in the collection.

Filtering removes the remaining small particles, including dust. Is this necessary?

Milk in first?

Carrying out a survey involves social skills: inviting people to take part, asking questions clearly, and in a way which encourages sensible answers.

For children to do

Is it better to put milk into the cup before pouring the tea, or to add the milk after the tea has been poured?
Many people have strong preferences.
Carry out a survey to find which people think they prefer. Encourage the children to help to design the survey. What questions should be asked? How can the answer be recorded?

Name	Do you like your milk in first or last?			Why?			In the test	
	First	Last	Don't mind	Tastes better	Looks better	Don't know	Right	Wrong
Anne		✓			✓			

Now make a pot of tea. Pour some cups with the milk in first, some with the milk in last. Label the cups. Stir well.

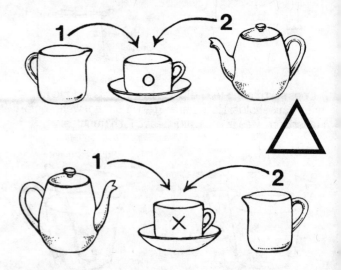

Use teaspoons for tasting. Test the people in the survey. Can they tell which is which?

To discuss

How well people were able to tell whether milk was added first or last. Did those who felt strongly about it do better than the others?
People can often tell if an unusual kind of milk has been used in tea. The children could test some of these: dried milk, homogenised milk, evaporated milk, long-life milk.

114

Dissolving sugar

Water soluble substances, like sugar, dissolve faster if the water is warm and if they are stirred, but they will eventually dissolve without either of these. More will dissolve in hot water than in cold water.

For children to do
Why do we put sugar in tea? What happens to it? What happens to the sugar? Does it disappear? Use the word *dissolve*. Does the sugar alter the taste of the water?

Sugar

How much sugar will dissolve in the hot water? It is surprising how much will, if it is stirred for long enough. To avoid a tediously long experiment use only a little water. Add 1 teaspoon of sugar, stir until it dissolves, add another teaspoon and so on until some remains undissolved. Keep a note of each teaspoon added.

Sugar

Coffee cup or 100 cc hot water

Will sugar dissolve in cold water? What happens to the sugar? Does it dissolve? Possibly go on to compare the time taken to dissolve in hot and in cold water.

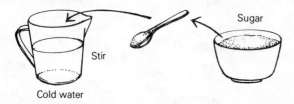

Sugar

Stir

Cold water

Why do we stir? Start both at the same time. Does stirring help things to dissolve?

Sugar

Warm water

Stir   Do not stir

If we use cold water and do not stir, will sugar ever dissolve? Ask the children to devise a test to find out. Try using a spoonful of sugar or a boiled sweet.

To discuss
The results of the tests: hot water and stirring help things to dissolve, but they will dissolve without these aids. If children have found out how much sugar will dissolve in 100 cc of water, can they deduce how much will dissolve in 200 cc?

More about dissolving things

Some substances are produced, or are found, in many forms. Sugar is a good example, each kind is used for a particular purpose.

For children to do

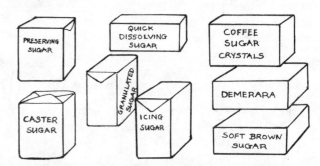

1. Collect different kinds of sugar. Use a magnifier to look at them. Do they look alike? What do they feel like? Smell like? Do they all taste the same.? Do the children think they will all dissolve in water? Ask each child to predict the one which will dissolve most easily. Record these predictions.

Help the children to devise a way of comparing the solubility of the sugars. Remind them to use the same amount of sugar, in the same volume of water, at the same temperature, stir them all. *Either* time them *or* start them simultaneously and compare, *or* count the number of stirs to dissolve them.

Predictions	
Jane	Quick dissolving
John	Soft brown

Order in the test	
1	
2	
3	

2. What else dissolves in water? Use warm water. Try bicarbonate of soda, coffee, rice, paint powder, salt, flour, chocolate, chalk, detergent powder. Can the children predict which will fall into each of these categories? Test to check the predictions.

Dissolved	Does not dissolve	Partly dissolves (like tea)

To discuss
Talk about the different kinds of sugar. What is each used for? Discuss the differences and similarities the children noticed. Discuss the children's reasons for their predictions. Was anybody right? Ask how undissolved solids can be separated from the liquid. Perhaps refer back to page 114. Discuss whether it is possible to get back something which has dissolved in water. How may this be done? Suggest evaporating water from a solution of salt, drying it out. Test to see if it works. Leave the solution in a warm place. Taste what remains.

How much sugar?

For children to do

1. Can people taste the difference between different amounts of sugar? How much sugar do the children like in their tea? Many people who take a lot of sugar do not stir it into their tea, and a lot is left in the bottom of the cup. Do they really need so much? How much sugar can people taste?

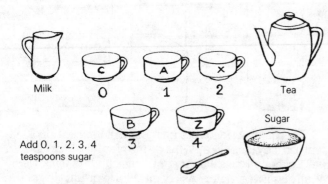

Milk

O
1
2
Tea

Add 0, 1, 2, 3, 4
teaspoons sugar

3
4

Sugar

Make a pot of tea and pour out five cups. Add milk as usual. Stir well until the sugar has dissolved. Label the cups. Now test people. First ask how much sugar they like in a cup of tea, then ask them to taste the tea in the 5 cups and choose the one they like best. Use teaspoons for the tasting test.

| Name | How many Teaspoons sugar in a cup of tea? | | | | | | Tea liked best | Teaspoons of sugar in tea liked best |
	Do not drink tea	0	1	2	3	4		
Peter	✓							complete this column last
John				✓			A	

2. Can people who like sugar in their tea tell if artificial sweeteners are used? Do all artificial sweeteners taste the same? To find the answers to these questions help the children to devise fair tests on the same lines as the one above.

To discuss

The sensitivity of taste. Can people distinguish different amounts of sugar? Does there seem to be a limit to the concentration they can distinguish? Could the people who did not take sugar tell if some was in their tea? Can people tell artificial sweeteners from sugar? People who do not take sugar can usually taste very small amounts. To find how little add 1 teaspoon to 500 cc water. When it has dissolved, ask somebody to taste it. If he can detect sugar, pour away half the solution and fill up again with water. This is now equal to ½ a teaspoon of sugar in 500 cc. Test again. Continue to dilute the solution in this way until the sugar cannot be detected. Each dilution halves the amount of sugar in the solution.

Tea stains

For children to do

How can tea stains be removed from tablecloths and clothes? Which washing powder is best? Make tea stains on some old pieces of white cloth. Use an old sheet. Drop exactly the same amount of tea onto each piece to be tested. Discuss why. Let the stains dry thoroughly. If they do not remember, remind the children that each stain must be tested in the same way. The only thing that changes is the kind of washing powder.

Same volume of water

At the same temperature

With the same amount of washing powder

Washed and rinsed in the same way

For the same time

And hung out to dry

To discuss

The results of the test. Which is the best washing powder for removing tea stains? Did the powder really help? What if the stains were simply soaked in water? Is the best washing powder for tea stains also the best for other things? The children could devise similar tests for coffee, ink and fruit stains and for grease marks. Which powder is best value for money? Consider quantity and effectiveness.

WEATHER RECORDS

Contents

This section is designed to help children with learning difficulties to become more aware of daily, weekly and seasonal change and pattern in the weather, and of the relationships between different components of the weather. It will help them to appreciate the influence of the weather on our activities, clothing and food supplies, and to understand weather forecasts. The text suggests a series of daily observations of the weather for the children to build up cumulatively over a period of at least three weeks, until they are able to compare their own daily record with the forecast weather.

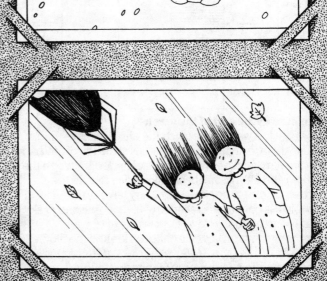

Week 1
Look at the sky

Decide the time in the afternoon when it will normally be convenient for the children to make their weather records. Additional morning records are needed only in the first week. Before you copy *recording sheet master 1* on page 122, modify it in any way you wish.

For children to do

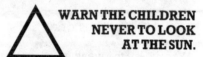

WARN THE CHILDREN NEVER TO LOOK AT THE SUN.

Discuss the way the sky outside could be represented on the chart. More than one symbol may be used, as in the example below. Are more symbols needed? Children might design their own. Leave one space blank for unexpected happenings, such as a hail-storm or a rainbow. Ask the children to make twice daily records on their individual chart and to fill in the symbols on a class copy of the chart.

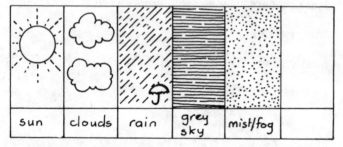

sun	clouds	rain	grey sky	mist/fog	

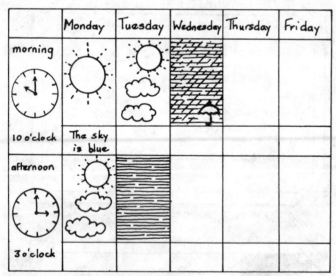

	Monday	Tuesday	Wednesday	Thursday	Friday
morning					
10 o'clock	The sky is blue				
afternoon					
3 o'clock					

To discuss at the end of the week

Talk about the weather records the children have made and use them to answer the questions at the top of the page. In particular, consider how the sky changed between the morning and afternoon observations. Try to help the children to remember the things they have seen, for example the colours and shapes of clouds, the kind of sky on rainy and on sunny days. Discuss the effect of sunny/rainy days on how the children feel, on the clothes they wear, on the games they play, on other things they do the effects of unusual amounts of rain, or droughts, on transport, water supplies, farming, fishing. What do we mean by *weather*? Start a weather dictionary.

Week 1
Other things to do

Warmth, winds and draughts and a large surface area all help water to evaporate.

1. Find the best drying place in the playground. Use wet pieces of cloth. Think about making the test fair: pieces of the same size, equally wet.

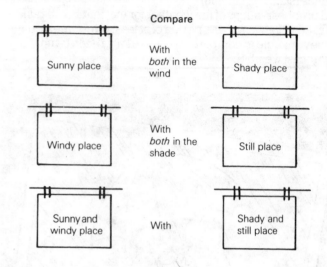

2. After rain, have a puddle drying competition. Ask pairs of children to choose either a puddle they think will dry up quickly or a puddle they think will last a long time.

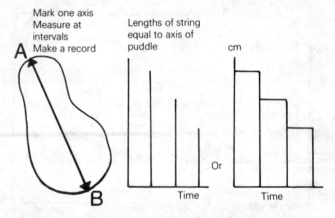

3. Where will water evaporate fastest in the classroom? Let the children try out their own ideas. To be fair, use one tablespoonful of water in each saucer.

To discuss

The results of the tests, and the conditions in each case which helped or hindered the evaporation of water.

See also *Me and my clothes*, Clothes to keep us dry, page 36. Learning Through Science, *Sky and Space*, the card *Clouds*, Macdonald, 1982.

Week 2
Do all the days feel the same?

If the children have not already been taught how to use a thermometer, you may prefer to take two weeks to do this work. In the first week record only the *feel* of the weather while the children learn how to use and read thermometers. In the second week add temperature readings to the daily records. See pages 126-128. If necessary, modify *recording sheet master 2*, page 123.

For the children to do

1. Discuss with the children the words weather forecasters use to describe how the days feel, for example, in winter, mild, cold, in summer, hot, warm, cool. Put two or three suitable words into the empty boxes on the left of the chart. Stress that each child should record what the days feel to him/her personally.

2. With the children, decide where the thermometer will be put and how it should be used. It should be at child's eye level in a protected *shady* place. If it cannot be permanently fixed, it should be put into position at least 10 minutes before the temperature is read.

3. Ask the children to fill in their own charts *every afternoon*. Morning readings are no longer needed. Add pictorial records to the class copy of the chart, for example a temperature chart.

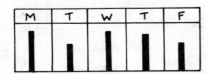

	Monday	Tuesday	Wednesday	Thursday	Friday
afternoon 3 o'clock					
mild	✓		✓		
cold		✓			
°C	9°C	4°C	12°C		

To discuss at the end of the week

Talk about this week's weather. Use the class charts to find the differences from last week. Ask how the weather has felt during the week. Do the children always agree? Try to show them that the feel of the weather does not always reflect the thermometer readings. Discuss how the children feel in hot/cold weather, the clothes they wear, the food they like. What effect has this weather on transport, sport, work?

Week 2
Other things to do

1. With the children, watch and discuss a demonstration of the water cycle. Children should not do this themselves. Go through the cycle of changes with the children. The droplets of water collect into pools if they settle on a cold surface, or evaporate into the air if they are kept warm. Let the children see this.

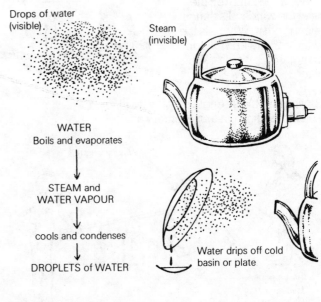

Drops of water (visible)

Steam (invisible)

WATER
Boils and evaporates
↓
STEAM and WATER VAPOUR
↓
cools and condenses
↓
DROPLETS of WATER

Water drips off cold basin or plate

2. Put a little cold water into a plastic sandwich box. Put on the lid and leave the box in a warm place for a few hours. What appears on the inside of the lid? Where has it come from?

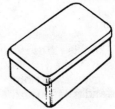

3. Stand a glass of iced water in a saucer in a warm room. What forms on the outside of the glass? Taste it. Where has it come from?

To discuss

The natural water cycle, and how it is related to the ones the children have seen with the kettle and sandwich box. The invisible water vapour which is in the air, and condenses into liquid on cold surfaces.

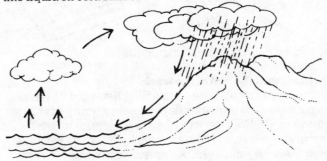

See also *Me and my clothes*, Clothes to keep us warm, Clothes to keep us cool, page 38.

Week 3
Think about the wind

Ground wind speed and direction are greatly affected by obstacles such as buildings, so recordings should be made in as open a place as possible. *Recording sheet master 3* is on page 124.

For children to do

1. Show the children the way the wind pulls things along with it. Where is the wind coming from? Drop a handful of dry grass. Which way does it blow?

2. Measure the strength of the wind.
(i) This method uses an arbitrary scale.

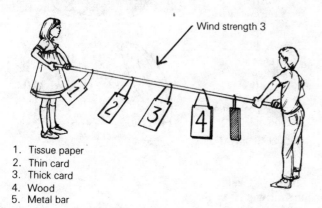

Wind strength 3

1. Tissue paper
2. Thin card
3. Thick card
4. Wood
5. Metal bar

(ii) Make a flag to use with *master sheet 4* on page 125 which gives a wind force range and is based on the Beaufort scale.

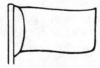

3. Find the direction of the wind. Two methods are shown. Winds are named according to the direction they come from.
(i) Use cotton to attach a small strip of light fabric to a long pole.
(ii) Use a shiny reflector to watch the clouds: mirror, or black tile, or rigid black plastic. A self-adhesive arrow shows the way the clouds are moving.

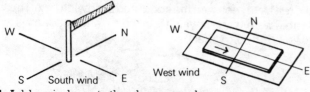

4. Add a windrose to the class records.

To discuss at the end of the week

Talk particularly about the wind. Which way did it blow on rainy days, on warm sunny days, on a very windy day? How strong was it? Does the wind make a difference to how *warm* we feel? How do the children feel in windy weather? How does the wind affect games and sports, ships, oil rigs, farming? What effect has it on transport, snowdrifts, fallen trees. Talk about unusual winds: gales, hurricanes, cyclones, tornadoes.

Week 3
Other things to do

1. Find out how trees, buildings, walls, fences and other obstacles affect the direction and strength of the wind. Use the methods described on page 121, or make windmills. Draw the diagonals and the 5 points marked with a dot. Cut 7 cm along each diagonal from the corner. Use stiff paper. Bring the corners to the centre and push a long pin through the 5 points marked with a dot, through a bead, into a balsa wood handle.

7 cm

Blow gently onto the windmill, then harder. It turns when it faces into the wind. Use the windmills to compare the speed and direction of the wind at different places. Make a record. Then mark the speed and direction of the wind on a plan or map

Place	Wind direction	Windmill speed		
		Slow	Medium	Fast
School gate	S		✓	

2. Make a windrose. Each day fill in a box in the direction the wind is coming from.

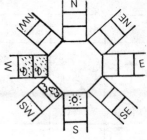

3. If you had no compass, how might you find north?

(i) Use the *sun*, which is in these positions.

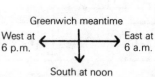

Greenwich meantime
West at 6 p.m. ← → East at 6 a.m.
South at noon

(ii) Find out about using the *stars*.

(iii) Is it true that moss grows only on the north side of tree trunks. Find out. Look at local trees.

To discuss

The need for windbreaks (crop protection, snow fences), the fact that an interrrupted barrier is more effective than a solid one, which just pushes the wind in another direction.

Week 4
Are weather forecasts right?

Each morning this week take to school a note of the weather forecast from the previous evening's radio or television programme, or from a morning newspaper. Pay special attention to the things the children have been observing. The children will need more copies of *recording sheet master 3*, page 124.

For children to do
1. Ask the children to watch the weather forecast each evening on television and try to make a record of the forecast. It is quite difficult to do this, and it might be easier if each child undertook to notice one thing. For instance, one might note what the day will feel like and the temperature, another the wind speed, and so on. Your own daily record of the forecast will almost certainly be needed as well.

2. Make a class display of the weather that is forecast for each day by filling in a week 3 chart. Every afternoon make weather observations exactly as in the previous week. Fill in a class chart. Compare the two charts. How good was the forecast?

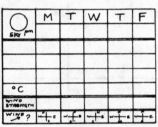
Forecast

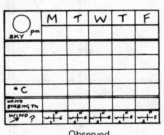
Observed

3. A few years ago an attempt was made to show the expected weather by means of the clothes people would need to wear, as in the illustration. An umbrella was added if rain was forecast. The children might like to invent their own clothes units and use them to show their forecast of the next day's weather.

To discuss at the end of the week
1. The reliability of weather forecasts. Why different people need to know what the weather will be. How the information is collected and the forecasts made. Satellite pictures. You might compare local forecasts with national ones, local papers and television stations usually give more accurate local forecasts.

2. Seasonal change during the four or five weeks of the observations. Compare the first week with the last. What sort of weather do we expect in this season?

Week 4
Other things to do

1. Collect sayings or rhymes which forecast the weather, such as the ones below.

Red sky at night, shepherd's delight;
Red in the morning, shepherd's warning.

Rain before seven, fine before eleven.

Last night the Sun went pale to bed,
The Moon in haloes hid her head,
'Twill surely rain – I see with sorrow
Our jaunt must be put off tomorrow.

Others make long-term predictions.

As the days grow longer the cold gets stronger.

If the cuckoo lights upon the thorn
Sell your sheep and keep your corn.
If the cuckoo lands on the blooming hip
Ditch your corn and keep your sheep.

If rain falls on St Swithin's Day, 15 July, it will rain for the following forty days.

Encourage the children to find more examples from books and by asking parents and grandparents. Compare them with official forecasts and the children's own observations. Are any of the sayings reliable?

2. Let the children use the telephone to find the local weather forecast. Remind them that when they dial the number they will interrupt a continuous recording of the forecast. They must wait for the beginning and then hear it through to the end. Is this forecast any more accurate than the previous evening's radio or television forecast, or than the one in the morning paper?

3. Discuss what the children now think is meant by *weather*. Compare their present understanding with the ideas they put forward in the first week of their work.

Further work on weather
Many other weather investigations are to be found on eight of the pupil cards in Learning Through Science, *Out of Doors*, Macdonald, 1982.

Recording sheet master 1

Week _____ **Name** _____

Sun	Clouds	Rain

Time	Monday	Tuesday	Wednesday	Thursday	Friday
Morning o'clock					
Afternoon o'clock					

Recording sheet master 2

Week _____

Name _____

Sun	Clouds	Rain

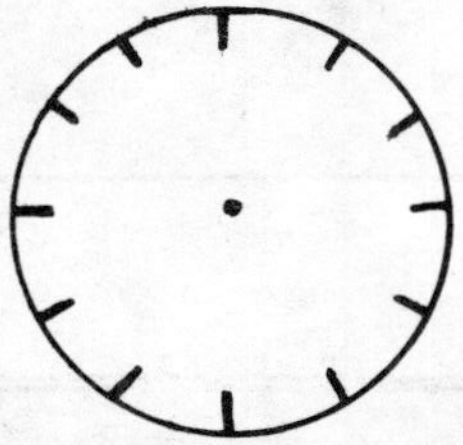	Monday	Tuesday	Wednesday	Thursday	Friday
Afternoon ___ o'clock					
°C					

Recording sheet master 3

Week   Name

Afternoon	Monday	Tuesday	Wednesday	Thursday	Friday
Sky					
°C					
Wind strength					
Wind	N W↔E S	N W↔E S	N W↔E S	N W↔E S	N W↔E S

Name		

Speed mph		Force
		0
	Leaves rustle	**1-2**
	Leaves blow about	**3-4**
	Big branches move	**5-6**
		7-8
		9-11

Thermometers

For children to use, a thermometer should be robust, easy to read and have a clearly marked, well spaced scale in degrees Celsius (Centigrade).

Wall thermometer
Glass tube on a protective wooden or polystyrene frame. Usually filled with red spirit. Range about −8°C to 50°C. Many also have a Fahrenheit scale which is easily covered with masking tape. Good for air temperatures. Relatively cheap.

Laboratory thermometer
Glass tube. Scale usually marked in black on yellow or white background. Usually contain mercury, but some have red spirit which is easier to see and safer. Range −10°C to 110°C. Wide range of use but rather fragile. To reduce breakages when opening the thermometer case always hold it horizontally; attach Sellotape flaps to thermometers and cases to stop them from rolling. Relatively cheap.

Master sheets to help children to learn to read these two types of thermometer are on pages 127 and 128.

Dial thermometer
Glass covered dial. A bi-metallic strip moves the indicator on the dial. Some models have the strip in a rod which can be put into liquids. Available in various temperature ranges. Robust, but more accurate models expensive.

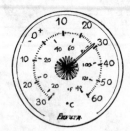

Osmiroid thermostick
A very robust dial type thermometer, claimed to be unbreakable. Made of stainless steel and plastics. Range −10°C to 120°C. Can be used for all school purposes. Expensive.

To help children to understand thermometers see Learning Through Science: *Out of Doors, How Hot?* (Pupil card and Teachers' Guide), Macdonald, 1982.

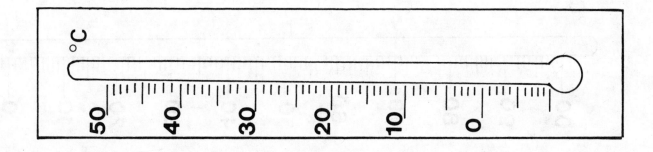

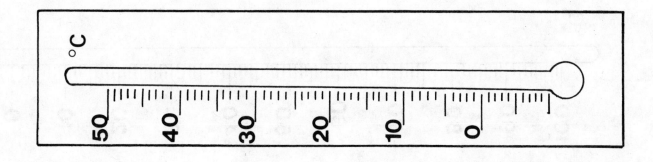

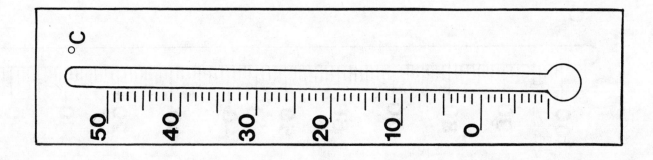

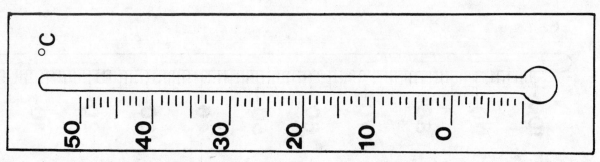

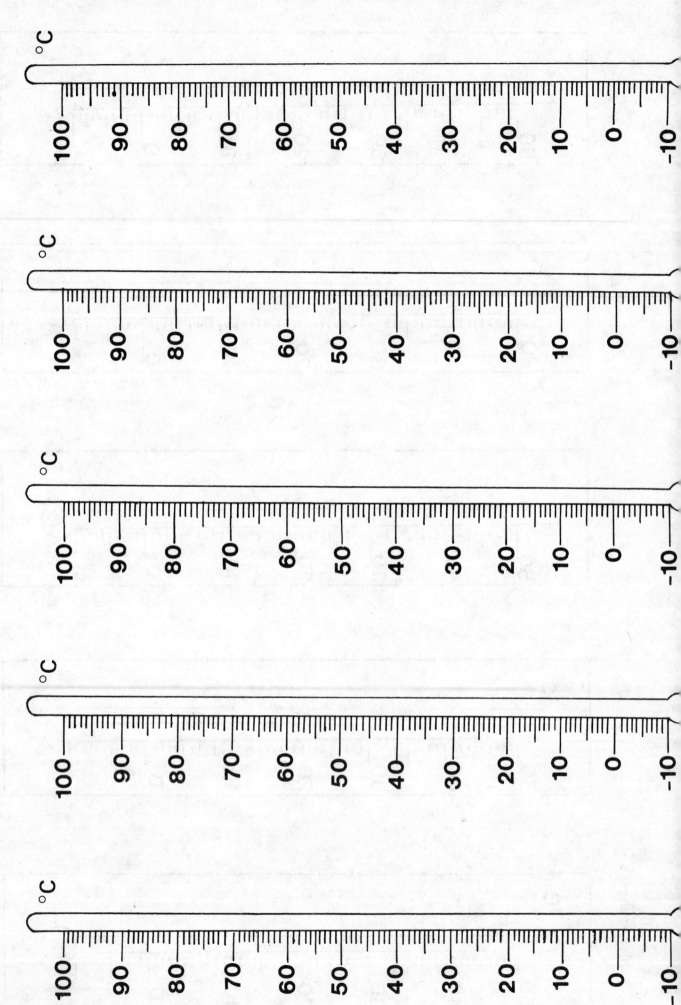

Master sheet 6